FITTER
STRONGER

Splendid

PUBLICATIONS

Fitter Stronger
Resilience – If You're Going Through Hell, Keep Going
By Paula Kerr

Splendid Publications Ltd,
1 Maple Place,
London W1T 4BB

www.splendidpublications.co.uk

British Library Cataloguing in Publication Data is available from The British Library

ISBN: 978-1-909109-79-7

Designed by Chris Fulcher at Swerve Creative

Printed and bound by Ashford Colour Press, Gosport, Hants PO13 0FW

Commissioned by Shoba Vazirani

Every effort has been made to fulfil requirements with regard to reproducing copyright material. The author and publisher will be glad to rectify any omissions at the earliest opportunity.

FITTER STRONGER

**Resilience –
If You're Going Through Hell,
Keep Going**

Paula Kerr

Splendid

PUBLICATIONS

For Michael, Holly and Daniel

CONTENTS

	Introduction	**7**
	Acknowledgements	**9**
1.	The Day That Changed Everything	**11**
2.	If You're Going Through Hell, Keep Going	**21**
3.	Why Fitter Stronger	**37**
4.	This Is Me	**51**
5.	Who Are You?	**67**
6.	Loss	**77**
7.	Managing Physical Change	**91**
8.	Youth Trauma	**103**
9.	Tell Me What You Want, What You Really, Really Want	**119**
10.	Be Kind To Yourself	**129**
11.	Sleep	**139**
12.	Exercise For A Vital You	**159**
13.	Exercise Routines	**177**
14.	Feed Your Engine	**207**
15.	Your Next Step	**237**
16.	Life Lessons	**245**

INTRODUCTION

*F*ITTER Stronger, Resilience - If You're Going Through Hell, Keep Going, is a practical guide to managing adversity by creating a strong, healthy mind and body. It identifies the vital coping mechanisms we all need when a grenade is thrown into our world.

Along with practical nutrition hacks and work outs for all abilities, there is advice on owning your situation and moving forward, from clinical experts and those who have been there.

I created wellness company Fitter Stronger following my own life changing run-in with breast cancer which I will explain here, along with my personal strategy for keeping my body strong throughout two years of treatment. The company which I'm delighted to say has become hugely successful, exists to promote exercise and nutrition as vital tools for illness, injury and trauma, to live a long, healthy, energetic life, with good mental health.

ACKNOWLEDGEMENTS

THERE is one person without whom this book wouldn't have happened, my friend and publisher, Shoba Ware, who believed I had something to say long before I did. Thank you for your gentle tenacity, patience and kindness.

A huge thank you to all those contributors, including Phil Hopley, Fred Wadsworth, Peter Venn and Singe Greene, who brought their knowledge or told their truth to help others.

Resilience is built through hard earned experience and I'm so grateful to my family and all of those friends who have come into my life to hold me up through the hard times and celebrate the wins. To name those I hold dear would be a book in itself but I must mention Anne-Marie Davies, Tracy Jollie and Angela Houghton, for always being there for my children, when cancer meant I couldn't.

To Simon Mackey, thank you for saving my life, rebuilding my body, keeping your promise to stay in my corner and holding my hand through my toughest fight.

I've been blessed to have a dedicated, talented team to work with and am especially thankful to Simon Jones, who encouraged my well-being ideas from the very start and stood at my side assisting, as each arm of Fitter Stronger was launched.

To Chase Coles, thank you for showing me how strong my body could be under pressure, so that I can now show others.

Finally, to my husband Michael, for climbing mountains with me, literally and figuratively, for always making everything alright and still making me laugh at your dreadful jokes all these years since you danced into my heart. And to our children, Holly and Daniel, for being the most gorgeous, loving, kind, sparky humans that any mum could wish for; you make me proud of you every day.

THE DAY THAT CHANGED EVERYTHING

February 12 2013 2pm

SIMON isn't smiling. He can't even look me in the eye. Each time I had met consultant plastic surgeon Simon Mackey to discuss breast reduction surgery, he was everything you want a surgeon to be – reassuringly calm, with a confident air and polished shoes. The shoes were important. It meant he paid attention to detail. And always smiling. But oddly, not today.

The surgery had gone well. I had healed quickly. I had a perky pair of breasts that suited my petite frame, quite a bonus in my 40s and our meeting was just a formality to agree all was well and close my file.

I had sat in the waiting room, happily, flicking absent-mindedly through a magazine, as I waited to be called. I arrived alone. I would be in and out. There was no need for anyone to be with me. No hand holding required. My friend Angela was collecting the children from primary school and I was retrieving them from her house on my way home. My husband Michael would arrive from work in the interim and I would cook dinner. It was a day much like any other.

When I was called in to his room by the nurse, I offered a cheery, 'Hello!' and for the first time Simon didn't look up from his desk. Instead he looked pained. 'While I was driving here,' he begins slowly, 'I was trying to find the right words to tell you this.' He paused and sighed. 'The tissue we removed was tested in the lab. And they found some abnormal cells.'

'What does that mean?' I asked. 'We believe they may be cancerous, but we need to find out more.' Simon winced as he spoke, knowing he was about to turn my life upside down. Just a couple of months earlier, he had risen through the ranks from senior registrar to consultant. I doubt he had been tasked with delivering such news previously and it clearly hurt him to do it. So, I'd had cancer without knowing it. The tissue that was cancerous had been removed during my breast reduction surgery two months earlier. I've had a lucky escape, I reasoned. I didn't even know I had cancer and probably I'm fine. I certainly feel fine. Well how lucky was that? But Simon didn't look as confident, his brow furrowed.

He introduced me to Sylvia Hurley, a petite Irish woman with a mop of curly dark hair, who had been sitting a few feet away. She explained that she was a breast cancer nurse, that she had some questions for me and some information about what happens next. Simon looked straight at me and followed up with, 'Whatever happens I will be here for you whenever you need me, for as long as you need me. I really mean that.' And I knew he did. As Sylvia ushered me away, to a room next door, I turned and looked over my shoulder at Simon, who looked stricken and told him, 'Don't worry, this is going to be absolutely fine.'

As we walked I ran this news through my mind. Breast cancer? You've got to be kidding. I've been training to climb Mount Snowdon. My ex-army personal trainer drives my body into the ground each week and I bounce back. I feel fitter than I have my whole life. I lift barbells, run competitively and have a hook in my office groaning under the weight of a heap of medals. If I was ill with cancer, I'd know about it, right? Maybe they've made some kind of mistake?

Sylvia sat me down on a wooden chair and explained that the tissue that had been routinely removed during my breast reduction operation revealed some abnormal cells that needed further investigation. To complicate matters, the lab no longer had all my removed breast tissue and it was impossible to know how many potentially cancerous cells may have existed. We went through my personal details as she filled out her forms: name, date of birth, address, blah blah. Sylvia explained that further investigation would be necessary to make sure nothing else sinister was lurking in my body. As this hadn't been a typical diagnosis – no lump, breast discharge, puckered nipple, altered areola, discharge, redness, misshappen breast, discolouration or other outward warning signs and the abnormal cells had happened by way of a kind of lucky post-op testing accident, no clear margins around my tumours had been established.

***

I sat quite calm, trying to take it all in. Sylvia talked about some tests, a bit of radiotherapy and meeting another doctor. I'd had a mammogram before my reduction surgery, as is routine. It had showed up nothing. Sylvia explained that as I'd had large 32GG breasts, it was possible cancer cells were too close to my chest wall to be detected.

My breasts had been the bane of my life. As a teenager, they grew quickly and soon became far too big for my frame. At 5ft 2 inches tall, I attracted the wrong kind of attention at work and in my social life. All the women in my family are busty but I received a particularly generous endowment. Now, once again, they were causing me worry and frustration.

I was a journalist on national newspapers, at a time when they were notoriously politically incorrect and I'd had to grow a thick skin. Not least when one morning in the news room of the *Daily Star*, a cocksure male reporter pinged my bra strap as he said 'Good morning.' Instead of my usual hunched shoulders as I tried to make myself smaller, I stood, pulled myself up to my full height and walked over to his desk. And I told him, just loud enough for the news desk to hear, 'If you ever dare do that again, I'll hang you out to dry,' before taking my seat, shaking in my shoes, tears of frustration stinging my eyes.

Exercise meant a very large sports bra on the tightest setting or I'd cause myself backache. I longed to wear pretty matching underwear. Instead, my bras were engineered to work like scaffolding, propping my huge breasts up to defy gravity. They were functional, like two hanging baskets strung together with super strong elastic.

After years of debate with my husband, who was reluctant to encourage any surgery that came with a level of risk, I finally persuaded him that I didn't want to see out my twilight years with back ache and permanent indentations on my shoulders where my thick bra straps had been. Although a breast reduction, which involved the removal of fat, glandular tissue and skin, was major surgery, it was commonplace and had a great reputation for a smooth recovery. And it would invigorate me. At age 43, it would mean I could reduce back, shoulder and neck discomfort. It would mean I could finally wear a dress — previously my chest was disproportionately large to my torso — and it would mean I could feel at peace with a body, which though strong, had embarrassed me for most of my life.

After a year of NHS hoop jumping to prove that I had thought this through, that my back, neck and shoulder pain couldn't be permanently fixed with physiotherapy or weight loss and that I met the strict body mass index target at every hospital weighing and measuring session, I was referred to my surgeon, Simon Mackey, at Queen Victoria Hospital, West Sussex. He was my final hurdle and he agreed to offer me surgery. An approximate new 32D cup size was agreed and a date for surgery was set.

I had no doubts about what lay ahead as consultant anaesthetist Colin Lawrence put a cannula into the back of my hand and made me smile as my body surrendered to anaesthetic. I recall him telling me he had no idea that when he went into medicine, he would spend much of his professional life discussing whether a newly formed breast was close enough to a C-cup.

My surgery was uneventful and as I had a peek inside my nightdress at my new pert breasts, I could barely believe they were mine and was absolutely thrilled. A summer of spaghetti strap vest tops lay ahead and I couldn't wait to embrace it.

As I emerged from my anaesthetic fog, Simon appeared at the foot of my hospital bed, to ask how I was feeling. I smiled and, a little drunk on analgesia told him, 'Loving your work!'

The 32GG bra I wore to hospital was consigned to the bin and the following day I wore a 32D bra for the first time and couldn't stop smiling, a heady mixture of vanity and relief that the surgery had gone well. A sports bra and long, green post-surgery compression socks were de rigueur 24 hours a day except during washing, for the next six weeks, until my check up and dismissal from Simon's clinical list. When I received a phone call to ask if I could bring my appointment forward by a week, I assumed my consultant was off on holiday and eagerly agreed, keen to ask if the post-op compression socks I had hidden under winter trousers could come off a little sooner, as spring was calling. I felt fit and well and very happy.

***

As I sat rationalising the information Sylvia gave me, the likely outcomes, the testing that lay ahead, I was doing quite well. Then she asked the killer question. 'Do you have children?' Oh hell. Tears poured down my cheeks. 'Yes, two,' I told her, as I unleashed uncontrollable sobbing. My son Daniel was aged nine. My daughter Holly was 11. And cancer was not going to stop me being their mummy, was it? It was Holly's 12th birthday in four weeks. We had a party planned, in a hall, with a DJ and all of Holly's friends. I had to be there. They mustn't know. Everything had to stay normal. Oh for fuck's sake. How the bloody hell am I going to manage this? All of it. The saying *life's what happens when you are busy making plans* had never been more true than it was at that moment.

Sylvia gave me a pile of pink breast cancer leaflets and explained that I would receive a letter telling me what would happen next and when I would meet my oncologist. I thanked her and stood up to leave, dazed and confused. I walked slowly to the lobby at Darent Valley Hospital, pulled my mobile phone out of my handbag and called my husband, Michael. 'Hey, can you come home a bit early? It's nothing to worry about but I need to talk to you without the kids being around.'

He agreed he would, of course and asked, 'Are you alright?' 'Yes, I'm fine,' I lied. My next phone call was to Angela. As promised, she had collected Holly and Daniel, the centre of my world, two little humans I was so proud of, from primary school for me, so I could get to hospital. My voice choked as I asked her to hold onto them for a little longer so I could talk to Michael in private. 'Yes of course, is everything alright?' Tears stung my eyes again, my voice cracked and I could just manage to say, 'No, no but I'll explain later,' before I hung up.

As I sat in the car and cried and cried, I thought back to Simon, who had looked devastated. No calm reassurance today. This wasn't good and now I had to wait for other people to decide what to do with me. There were no real answers at this stage. There was just a heap of worry, lots of maybes and talk of a multi-disciplinary team meeting later that week, where surgeons, oncologists and breast cancer nurses would gather to discuss my fate. So how do I explain that to my husband? As I drove home, I made a decision that I would absolutely not tell our children. They need never know. My own childhood had been chaotic and I had absolutely no desire to throw a cancer grenade into their young lives.

***

I was in the kitchen unloading the tumble drier when Michael arrived home, dropped his bags in the hall and walked hurriedly towards me, asking what happened at the hospital. Composed, I calmly explained that the breast reduction operation was completely successful but that it uncovered what are likely to be cancer cells in my tissue, that the tissue had been removed in the breast reduction operation but that they wanted to do a few more tests to double check all is ok. The most likely scenario is a bit of radiotherapy, to mop up any other rogue abnormal cells that may still be lurking.

'So that was weird. I had breast cancer and never even knew it. And now it's gone. Sorry for getting you to leave work early, but I didn't want to tell you with the kids running around,' I told him, with minimum fuss. He accepted this, gave me a hug and I went to collect the children. I wanted to get on and get dinner ready, the same as usual. I wanted everything to be normal.

Holly and Daniel were playing in the garden with Angela's children when I arrived and she put the kettle on to make tea. 'I guessed something was wrong. How did Michael take it?' she asked. Well, good question. Michael is the worrier of the two of us and he was remarkably calm and unquestioning. I asked Angela to keep this maybe-I-have-cancer-maybe-I-don't news quiet, which she promised she would. I hadn't absorbed it myself yet and had no idea what its repercussions would be, so I wasn't going to tell anyone else yet and even then, it would be on a need to know basis.

My son was kicking a football into the net in Angela's garden as we watched from her kitchen window. My daughter was chatting to Angela's daughter, Ella. The sun was shining. Their world was happy, content. As I called them in to go home for tea, I wanted it to stay like that. Forever. I could take whatever was to be thrown at me. But I needed to protect them. I couldn't be responsible for their unhappiness. Damn all of this.

**

The next day I went to the gym where I met my ex-army personal trainer, Chase Coles and we went into a side room, so that I could tell him my news. Other than Michael and Angela, I hadn't told anyone else and getting the words out wasn't easy. I kept repeating that I didn't know how this was going to work out but that I needed to keep my body strong. Chase made me a promise that he would stay in my corner for as long as I needed him. He's a man mountain with a heart of gold. As I walked away and sat on an exercise bike, not feeling much like exercising but trying to make my body reassure me that somehow everything was fine, tears pricked my eyes. I pedalled faster and faster, trying to block out the whirring uncertainty in my brain and stop the tears. It wasn't much of a work out that day but it helped a bit and brought my shoulders back down from my ears.

**

After a series of tests, ultrasound, MRI and biopsy, my first appointment was with Seema Seetharam, my oncology surgeon, a short, stout woman who hadn't checked her notes for my name and had to ask me who I was as she flicked through the pages of my file. As a journalist, if I had turned up to an interview with no clue about the person standing in front of me, I would have been annihilated by both the interviewee and my editor. I let it go as she explained that I would need an operation to investigate my lymph nodes. An incision would be made in my armpit and some nodes would be removed for testing. 'It's just belt and braces, we won't find anything,' she said confidently. 'It's nothing to worry about. It's a quick operation and you can go home the same day.' Well that was a little light in a tunnel of uncertainty. She seemed pretty sure that there would be no cancer in my lymph nodes and at least it would be quick.

A week later, Michael dropped me off at Darent Valley Hospital and I was admitted for day surgery, given a standard blue gown to change into, sat on a bed and wheeled into the pre-op room for anaesthetic. A vicious pantomime ensued where two nurses heatedly argued across my bed and repeatedly failed to get a cannula into my arm to administer my anaesthetic, spitting blood onto my gown and the sheets. After five minutes I shouted that they must stop and find someone else or I was walking out. A third nurse arrived, the cannula successfully entered into my vein and anaesthetic was administered before I had a chance to grow any more anxious.

***

Within an hour I was sat up in bed in the recovery room. After a short while Seema Seetharam arrived at my side. She explained that the operation had been straightforward and without complication. The anaesthetic that had taken so long to administer an hour earlier had worn off completely and I wanted to go home. An exhausted recovery room nurse told me that it was procedure to move me to a ward, from where I would be able to be discharged. She also told me that operations were being cancelled because there was no room on the wards and so no room in the recovery room, either. So I asked for my clothes and bag and told her she could either discharge me herself from the recovery room or I was leaving anyway. 'Leave it with me,' she said and returned five minutes later with a pink discharge form for me to sign and a key to the locker holding my things, glad of an empty bed. I called Michael and asked him to pick me up as I wasn't allowed to drive.

***

Two weeks later, I was back in Seema Seetharam's office. Tests had revealed cancer cells in my lymph nodes. 'You said, belt and braces. You weren't expecting to find anything,' I challenged, alarmed. Chemotherapy was now a possibility. I was told that I was to be discussed at the next hospital multi-disciplinary meeting when a decision would be made about my treatment path and to wait for a letter. As she walked away as if she'd just told me that the milkman wouldn't be delivering that week, my mind was racing. Yes I wanted chemo to kill the cancer cells. But it would be brutal. How would I hide that from my children? So far, I'd made sure fish finger Fridays still happened, bed time stories were read, school runs and homework were delivered and everything in their world was normal. I wasn't going to have to destroy that, was I? I gathered four of my closest friends around me and explained my new reality, that I needed them to keep it to themselves and that my children mustn't know. They offered to help with school runs I might be absent for and promised to keep their counsel. That weekend, Holly's party, held jointly with her friend Olivia, passed off seamlessly. Olivia's mum Anne Marie and I pulled it together. I made dozens of cupcakes, piped with chocolate icing, Michael drew life size pictures of the girls on rolls of wallpaper liner, we laid out the buffet in the village hall, balloons adorned the room, music played with disco lights as children and parents danced and I stood in the middle of it, smiling on the outside and completely empty on the inside, wondering how much longer I could keep up this everything's-fine-and-normal charade.

***

A letter arrived two weeks later, inviting me to an appointment with my oncologist, Andrew Visioli. By the time we met, I wanted the strongest drugs he had and I was prepared to take whatever side effects that meant. A dour man, he looked as though he had picked his crumpled beige suit up off the floor that morning. We agreed that my aggressive grade 2 HER2 positive breast cancer would be blasted with three rounds of FEC chemotherapy, followed by three rounds of FEC-T chemotherapy, administered every three weeks. This would be followed up with 18 rounds of targeted chemotherapy Herceptin. I would be in the chemo ward at regular intervals for the next two years. I was hungry for answers. How did chemo work on my particular cancer? Why was he prescribing this particular kind? What was the success rate? Would I lose my hair? Would I feel sick? I was his worst nightmare. As a journalist for most of my adult life, I had sought facts and evidence. In the waiting room, I had watched his previous patients emerge from his office, grateful and compliant. But I needed to know everything. This was a long, scary journey I was embarking on and I wanted to be armed with as much information as possible. I told him I had been looking into nutrition and intended to exercise as much as I sensibly could during my treatment and eat really clean. I was going to meet cancer head on. He swung his swivel chair away from his desk, rested his elbows on his knees, leaned forwards and said nine words so damning that I will never forget them. 'There's nothing you can do to change your situation.' Say what now? Well fuck you, Mr Visioli. I may not be able to change my diagnosis but I am absolutely taking control here. I said nothing as we left but I was furious. I was absolutely not going to roll over and let cancer take down my body and soul. As we walked to the car, Michael tried to calm me down but I'd never been so mad. Mad with cancer, mad with my oncologist, mad with all of it.

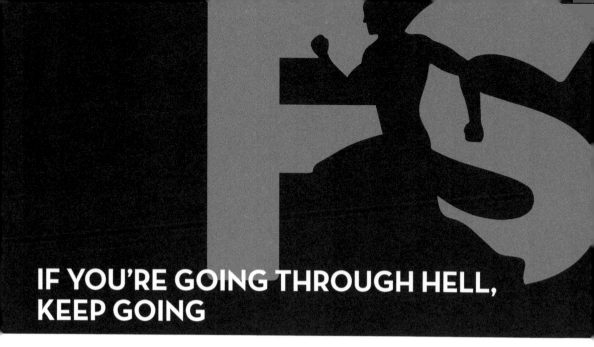

IF YOU'RE GOING THROUGH HELL, KEEP GOING

The Long Dark Tunnel

THERE were days over the next two years when I seemed very lost in a long, dark tunnel, with nothing but a dim, barely flickering light ahead. I had two choices: dive under the duvet, carry on crying and feel helpless, or get back up and fight each time I got knocked down. A couple of times I chose the former. Mostly I chose the latter. I held onto that light, trusted that it would eventually burn brighter and that I'd be out of the tunnel. Friends were generous in their offers of help and well meaning in their encouragement but they weren't sitting where I was. This was my fight and none of them could have it for me.

How we choose to react in crisis is referred to as 'fight or flight'. Stand your ground or run to the hills. That reaction is influenced by our memory of previous trauma, explains consultant psychiatrist Dr Phil Hopley. His training in forensic, general and sport psychiatry, combined with a career playing premiership rugby, has enabled him to develop his passion for the mental health of elite performance in sport and business, guiding mental health strategy, development and providing coaching and crisis support. He says, 'Fight or flight is a biological response that is hardwired into all humans and it has been with us since time began. It's a defensive or protective mechanism. In situations where we feel threatened, we will respond physically. The brain reacts to the threat by releasing cortisol. The release of cortisol, then releases adrenalin and our body goes into fight or flight mode. Some people call it fight, flight or fear, as some of us feel immobilised by fear. Fight means you are going to take something on. Flight means you are going to run away from it. To do either of those we need energy supplied to the big muscles in our arms and legs, to our heart and lungs to control our breathing and most importantly, we need to direct our attention onto the threat.

'Not only is there a variation in response between people,' he adds, 'there is also a variation in response within the same person. Similar circumstances can provoke very different responses. This is predominantly down to our learned experiences and how we become conditioned over time. It's an automated response. What has been happening in the past? It all comes down to perception. How are we perceiving what's happening in front of us? Are we perceiving it as a threat? If so, it will trigger the fight or flight response. Our response is linked to success we have had in similar situations in the past. Our brains are very good at remembering good and bad experiences and drawing on them when we are under pressure.'

***

Up for the Fight

After my initial shock diagnosis, I made up my mind I was up for the fight. But not every day was positive. Far from it. On dark days, I held on to a few mantras. One of them, *'If you're going through hell, keep going'* is attributed to Winston Churchill, during the Battle of Dunkirk, in World War II. This was my war on cancer. I couldn't go back and there was no escape, I had to keep going. I thought that often. Another mantra was Abraham Lincoln's *'One day at a time.'* On bleak days, I'd remind myself not to look back, as there was no point, I wasn't going there. And not to look too far ahead and catastrophise. Instead, just deal with the here and now. Just get through today. Then try again tomorrow. It's a useful brain trick. When I work with clients, whatever their situation, we start by chunking down their goals into manageable bites, then move forward.

Shortly after that last meeting with my oncologist Andrew Visioli, and following a nerve wracking abdominal ultrasound to search for further cancer cells, which was mercifully negative – my first bit of good news – my first chemotherapy session was in my diary and our Easter family holiday to Crete was cancelled. Conversations were had with our children's head teachers and promises made that they would update us if either of them were teary or distressed at school. And I went wig shopping, pulling on a variety of styles, lengths and colours at the Hot Hair concession in Selfridges, with a kind assistant, until I found one I could bear, similar to my own shoulder length auburn bob, that would see me inconspicuously through work meetings and the occasional restaurant visit, after I would inevitably lose my hair – the part of this whole sorry saga I was looking forward to least. It would be a stark reminder in the mirror each morning of this cancer madness.

When I got home, I took my wig to show my dear friend and next door neighbour Wendy. A hairdresser, she had been diagnosed with terminal lung and liver cancer the previous year, had already lost her hair once and had lots of practical wig advice. I was one of the first to be told her diagnosis and she mine. She was also a great reminder, though she would never say it, that I was lucky. I had aggressive breast cancer but I wasn't terminally ill. Wendy did her best to encourage me, with varying degrees of success, to be a patient patient.

***

May 17 2013

If I'm honest, I was in denial. Here I was, in the Pine Therapy chemo unit at Darent Valley Hospital, sat in a semi circle with men and women of all ages, who looked sick. I felt fine. Like a fraud. Or the result of a dreadful mistake. I was given the option of a PICC line (peripherally inserted central catheter) that would remain in my arm permanently until my treatment ended or a cannula in my arm that would be removed after each visit. I reasoned that I would surrender to being a cancer patient all the time I was on the ward, but I wanted as few reminders of it as possible when I walked out the hospital door and so opted for the latter.

Michael took me to hospital, waited patiently for the rest of the day while the children were collected by my friends for play dates after school, and drove me home. Later, I felt fine and cooked dinner. But I had no appetite and a rising anxiety was tying my stomach in knots. I knew it was a matter of days before I lost my hair, at least partially and I needed to tell our children that Mummy has cancer and I'm fine but my hair will fall out. I decided to get the words out at the end of dinner, that night. I rehearsed what I was going to say in my head, wore my best smile and reassured them that nothing would change in their world. I made a joke about wigs and hats but no one was laughing. My son Daniel was silent and left the table to play with his toys in his bedroom. Holly went to her room, too. I checked on them and Daniel was absorbed in his Nintendo DS. Holly couldn't hold back the tears and asked me if I was going to die. I told her the truth as I understood it, which was that I would do everything in my power to make sure that didn't happen.

As I left hospital, with a bag of anti-sickness drugs, I was handed a pack of retractable needles and a sharps bin. Following chemotherapy, I would need to inject myself daily with filgrastim, a medication to boost my white blood cell count which would have been impacted by chemo. The poor ward nurse saw the colour drain from my face at the thought. So after I'd checked on the children, I retreated to our bedroom and locked the door. I pinched my thigh skin, as instructed, injected and quickly popped a chocolate mint, on standby and not standard NHS issue, in my mouth to confuse my senses, while I put the used needle in the yellow sharps box, hidden in my wardrobe. The nurse called the next day to make sure I was ok, which I was, though I never got used to it.

***

My Crowning Glory

The next day I was rushing the children out the door to school when, as I pulled my shoulder length, dark brown hair away from my face, a heap of strands were left in my hand. With a sharp intake of breath, I pushed them into my pocket. The hair loss had started already.

After the school run I went to the gym for a training session with my PT, Chase. He asked how I was feeling and I could just about get the words out that I was feeling pretty damned awful. Physically I was OK but mentally I was ruined after the dreadful confessional to my children the night before that I would never forgive myself for. I knew that once that genie was out of the bottle there was no pushing it back in and I hadn't slept. After a treadmill warm up, Chase put a 15kg bar on my shoulders and asked me to squat and stand. He added two 5kg plates to the bar and asked me to squat again. Several more plates were added. When we finished, he asked me how strong I was feeling. The answer, of course, was a great deal stronger than when I arrived.

I went downstairs to the changing room to shower. As I blow dried my hair, lots of thick brown curls fell to the floor. I was alone and quickly swept it up, pulled on a hat and left. I knew this was coming but I still felt like I'd been punched in the stomach. How would the children react?

The next day I was due to run a race I normally thoroughly enjoyed, the five mile cross country Harvel 5, near my Kent home, with two lovely friends, Karen and Donna, two far better runners than me, who promised to get me to the finish line and that we would cross it together. It's always held on the first Sunday in June at 2pm and notorious for being ludicrously hot. I had already made a decision to have my head shaved once my hair started to fall out, reassured by my oncologist that it would grow back. I didn't want to keep finding clumps of it on my pillow or in the shower. As I sat in the gym car park, I called my hairdresser. We arranged that I would go to her house early the next morning, which I did, after yet another sleepless night. As she got to work, I watched as my hair fell to the floor, along with my tears and then hers. She gave me a hug. I pulled my wig on and went home. I showed my husband who reassured me that I rocked a shaven head and my children, who were less impressed and horrified that I would be seen in public with no hair at the race later that day.

Lots of friends and neighbours would be at the event, I reasoned and it was a good opportunity to let everyone see what was happening at the same time, instead of having endless conversations. I'd had to say 'I have cancer' plenty of times already and it wasn't getting any easier. I arranged to meet Donna and Karen at the start line and gave another friend, Tracy, my baseball cap to hold while I ran. As I removed it from my head, I studied her reaction. She smiled and told me it suited me. Others likened me to Demi Moore as GI Jane. Nobody threw up their arms in horror or cried or gave me a sad face. I can so do this, I thought.

I had stuck to my exercise and nutrition regime as much as possible and felt strong as we passed the mile markers, with lots of cheers along the way and big hugs at the end. My children were still mortified that I looked very different in front of their friends but relaxed as their friends took it in their stride, as children do. It wasn't my fastest time but it was certainly my most memorable race. I had this cancer thing down. That night my son refused a hug until I put my hat on. He told me I wasn't his real mummy. That lasted a couple of heartbreaking days, until the hugs became hat free and more frequent once again.

The following week, Holly was set to go away with school for a residential week of outdoor activities. The head teacher, Carolyn Howson, now a dear friend, agreed to break the rule of no contact with parents during this time and promised Holly could call any time she wanted to. She called three times, Carolyn resolutely marching around the grounds in the dark, late at night with Holly, until they found a mobile phone signal, for which I will always be grateful.

***

Michael and I got into a pattern with chemotherapy sessions. He would take me and wait for the duration of the agonising bit while the needle went into my hand. This became progressively more difficult as the chemo thinned my veins and the needles couldn't progress. More and more options were sought until my left arm looked like a pin cushion. My record was five needles and a few tears before we found a vein that would grudgingly accept a cannula. My right arm had to be kept free for further blood tests needed before and after each chemo and driving whenever I felt able to. With the cannula in place, Michael would pop to

Costa Coffee and buy me a wholegrain sandwich with roasted vegetables, which I would force down, in a bid to create some energy in my body. I'd then send him off to collect me later. I'd open my survival bag: newspaper, Kindle, pen, notebook, tissues, fruit jellies, aromatherapy oil roller to dab onto my right wrist – a great antidote to the clinical smell of the ward - iPod, headphones and phone and get into my own world. There was little conversation between patients, stoically enduring their own private hell. I tried to ignore the trill of dozens of machines that would signal that bags of life-saving poisonous fluid needed changing. Now and then a well meaning hospital visitor would stand over me, with pity in their eyes, asking if I needed to talk. They would go to each patient in turn. I politely but firmly told them I was fine, thanks. I wasn't of course but I had my plan for the day and it didn't involve their pity face.

***

June 28 2013

The half way point was a great milestone. It meant I could count down the last three rounds of FEC T chemo, which were particularly tough. As the chemo entered my body it became harder to bear. I could feel my energy draining away as the red FEC T poison dripped into my system. I dreaded those sessions and ached for them to end. It always meant a slow stagger back to the car and straight home to bed. It was summer in Pine Therapy ward now, which was situated in the hospital basement. The chemo room was stifling. My shaven hair had completely fallen out and I looked like an egg.

The recovery time took longer, up to 10 days before I could get to the gym. In the meantime I tried to eat well, despite my sense of taste disappearing, along with my appetite. I stopped eating food for enjoyment and forced it down like fuel for my flagging engine. Like this whole cancer scenario, this was easier some days than others. At my weakest, I needed two hands pressed against the walls to get from the bedroom to the bathroom, very slowly. I was tired, sick and weepy and managed six oven chips all day, brought to me in bed by Michael. He had cooked a few extra when he made dinner for our children and was anxious that I should eat something, anything.

As soon as possible, I would return to the school run, so that Michael could work, keen to keep life as normal as possible for our children. At my lowest, I remember it taking a full 10 minutes to walk the short distance from my car and up the steps to the playground, where I retreated under the trees, pulled my white baseball cap down to my eyes, exhausted and shed silent tears, quickly brushed away when Holly emerged from class, a bundle of sunny energy, asking if we could just pop home and grab towels and swimming costumes, for an after school impromptu pool party at her friend Sophie's house. She may as well have asked if we could just pop up to the top of K2. Olivia's mum Anne Marie saw my anguished face and stepped in before I could speak. 'Hey, Olivia has lots of spare swimming costumes, why not pop back with us for tea and I'll take you, Holly?' Two play dates in one, what luck, Holly eagerly agreed. And I was more grateful than she'll ever know, to be able to stagger back to the car and home to curl up on the sofa with Daniel, while she took care of Holly's fun.

**

When I could get to the gym, I worked on building up my strength, sometimes with Chase, sometimes alone. Always with a friendly nod from the gym staff and my gym buddies, who had my back but didn't intrude on my private time. This is where I came to clear my head. No wig, no hat, no hair, no eyelashes. It was the place I could just be me. The drive took 30 minutes. I wasn't sleeping so I was there when the doors opened. Sometimes I'd sit on a bike and pedal slowly for 10 minutes until I was exhausted but it was more than I had done the day before. That was progress. The next day I would pedal again and maybe try a bit of rowing or lift some light weights. The next day I'd increase the weights. On good days I'd join a spin or circuit class and do what I could. I remember a lady in the circuit class always needing to pop to the loo when burpees were announced. She turned to me one day and said, 'Well if you're doing them, I suppose I'll have to,' and winked, which made me smile. I'd build myself up until the next chemo dose took me back to square one.

After the battering my arms had taken in the chemo ward, my legs were stronger, so I'd ask someone to put a bar on my back so that I could squat and take it off when I'd finished as I couldn't lift it myself. On bad days, days full of frustration, anxiety and anger, I'd find one of my gym buddies, Darren, and say, 'Gloves and pads?' He'd hold the pads and I'd jab cross them for all I was worth, sometimes through tears, until I couldn't punch anymore. A semi-professional boxer, he told me if I was going to have a fight, I might as well have it properly and started to teach me how to box. At over six feet and with much broader shoulders and longer arms than mine, he barely flinched as I fought but I always felt so good afterwards. Midway through chemo I was supposed to climb Mount Snowden with friends and was mad as hell that I had to cancel. Those lovely friends promised they would climb with me the following year, when I was stronger. And I would hold them to that promise, but more of that later.

***

Between trips to the chemo ward, blood tests, and chemotherapy, the conversations about a mastectomy began with my oncologist, my oncology surgeon, Seema Seetharam and plastic surgeon, Simon Mackey. I reasoned that as I definitely had cancer in at least one breast, with no clear margins around the tumours, uncovered by chance through tissue testing following my breast reduction surgery, the tissue had been discarded and there was more cancer in my lymph nodes, I wanted both breasts removed and reconstruction surgery, where tissue would be moved from my stomach to my chest to create two new breasts. My oncologist argued that drug therapy was enough and I should follow chemotherapy with radiotherapy. He said a mastectomy wasn't necessary. His actual words were, 'You might as well cut off your right leg.' My oncology surgeon countered that although my pathology was unusual, there was no obvious cancer in my left breast and she wouldn't remove healthy tissue and therefore would not carry out a double mastectomy but a single mastectomy on my right breast was important. My plastic surgeon, true to his word all those months ago, said he would do whatever surgery would give me peace of mind, which was what I craved most of all. The rows between Seema Seetharam and I – her digging her heels in that I should have a single mastectomy and me insisting on a double mastectomy in case my cancer returned and set up home in my left breast (I'd heard so much anecdotal evidence) – happened in her evening clinics, which typically ran up to two hours late. I was still having chemotherapy and would lay down on the cold, metal outpatients waiting room chairs, exhausted, unable to sit upright, with my head rested on Michael's lap. We argued, disagreed and I'd go home, worn out and frustrated.

***

The Home Stretch

My final FEC 2 chemo took place in September. My oncologist Andrew Visioli told me I would be on my knees at this point but the clean eating and exercise regime he dismissed, together with a heady happiness that this chemo type was at an end, had put a spring in my step. The light in that long tunnel was finally starting to shine a little brighter. I celebrated that night, sharing a pizza in bed, with my lovely children either side of me and a very small glass of champagne. Not strictly allowed, nor recommended but necessary. A restorative week in south Devon followed, during the children's half term holiday. Sitting by the sea, splashing in the surf, fishing for mackerel with my little family and feeling the sun on my face, away from any hospitals, was the very best tonic.

On our return, the surgery fight raged on, however. At one point, I gave in and said I would have the right breast removed and reconstructed in the same operation. I had no fight left in me. I just wanted to have this whole scenario ended as soon as possible. The day before the operation, in November, Simon Mackey called me into his clinic and pleaded with me for over an hour to reconsider, knowing that this course of action wouldn't give me peace of mind. He'd promised in February to do whatever he could to help me and he truly meant it. With his support I changed my plan. Seema Seetharam conceded that I could have a mastectomy in my right breast, which she would perform, with a temporary implant put in place by Simon, to keep the shape of the skin pocket. If I still felt strongly about it, I could return a year later, have a mastectomy of my left breast and reconstruction on both sides at the same time, using tissue from my stomach.

The mastectomy surgery was relatively straightforward. I was reassured to see the same kind anaesthetist, as I lay on the operating table, this time with no hair, no eyebrows and feeling ugly and vulnerable. My recovery was swift and I was home three days later. Peeking under my nightdress this time didn't bring the same joy as it had after my reduction surgery. I had just one perky breast left and knew that its life was to be short lived. But it was a step in the right direction for my long-term well-being.

After convalescence, I was back to the chemo ward to commence my new drug, Herceptin. A targeted chemotherapy, which hunts for cancer cells like a heat seeking missile, instead of taking down cancer cells along with healthy ones like FEC chemotherapy had, it's now administered swiftly with an injection. However, it was available intravenously only when I had it and there was a risk to my heart function, which needed to be checked regularly. At my first heart scan, after a particularly satisfying boxing session two hours earlier, the echocardiogram operator told me my heart was poorly functioning and that my Herceptin treatment would have to stop. I hadn't come this far to be stopped in my tracks and challenged his verdict. I spent the rest of the day at the hospital, bothering my oncologist and a cardiologist until the matter was resolved and it was agreed that the echocardiogram was poorly functioning, my heart was perfectly fine and my drug treatment could continue. The good news about Herceptin was that other than the heart risk and a general lethargy, the side effects were less severe. Though I would require 18 doses, so my trips to the chemo ward, wired to machinery, succumbing to being a patient, were far from over, as was the no brie, no alcohol, no smoked salmon rule imposed on diagnosis, as if to add insult to injury.

***

Christmas was small, simple, at home with family and very special. 2014 saw
a pattern of working from home, interviewing over the phone, writing small
magazine features and occasional exhausting visits to London for press junkets.
I walked into a room for the season launch of BBC drama *Silk*, with Rupert Penry
Jones and Neil Stuke, both of whom I'd interviewed many times. Neil looked
concerned as he caught my eye. Rupert took one look at my short hair regrowth
and asked, 'Wow, what happened to you?' before giving me a hug and checking
I was OK. I'd got used to people dancing around my illness, not sure what to say.
Rupert made me laugh out loud and his hug was warm and kind.

Another time, a publicist friend organised an interview with Michael Bolton, who
I'd also met often. She must have told him my situation and the following day a
huge trough of orchids arrived to be signed for, with the sweetest note attached.
As my energy gradually returned, there were also afternoon teas with lovely
friends and walks in the woods. This may have been my fight but I had one hell
of an army behind me. My chief of staff was my husband, Michael. While I was
battling, he felt helpless, unable to take my pain away. A gardener and garden
designer, he admitted he chopped a lot of logs when he was at work, just so that
he could sleep.

***

Getting Stronger

Every three weeks I'd drive myself to hospital for Herceptin treatment and blood
tests after the school run and drive home again. I'd get to the gym as often as
possible and grew increasingly interested in exercise for recovery. I tried to find
myself a wellness holiday that catered for those who had an illness and wanted to
improve their strength but couldn't. There were heaps of yoga retreats and boot
camps but nothing for someone like me, who enjoyed exercise and wanted lots
of information about what to eat and how best to train to put my body in the
strongest possible position to cope with a debilitating condition. A friend booked
us a spa day but I was turned away at the door. When I completed their health

Q&A, they refused to paint my nails, much less give me a massage, despite my oncologist agreeing that the amount of chemotherapy my body withstood meant a little almond oil was never going to pose a threat.

As the months ticked by, both children settled, with the odd tear and request for reassurance. Although their mum looked a bit different, their life continued as normal, with school, play dates and tennis, drama, cricket and football runs at the weekends. My daughter Holly, now in secondary school, came home one day and announced that she would audition for the school play and hoped to get into the chorus. The following day she said she was successful and I was delighted that she had a distraction that made her happy and lots of new school friends.

Regular check-ups, scans and blood tests continued. Otherwise, life was returning to a new kind of normal, although the second mastectomy operation, with reconstruction, lay just months away and I needed Seema Seetharam to confirm she would do it as she had promised. I was also very aware that my body had already been through a great deal, that this was major surgery and I was starting to admit to myself that I was scared. Scared enough to visit our village vicar Chris. Far from a text book vicar, we first met at the rugby club, where he was playing drums in a rock band at the local music festival. He did all the regular vicar things: communion, dog collar, judging the local primary school art competition but he didn't damn you to hell for failing to attend his church, which I only ever did at Christmas, and we had always got along well. I presented Chris with a detailed plan for my funeral, as we sat on a bench in the churchyard, a CD of the music I wanted played and he showed me where I would be laid in the churchyard should anything go awry under anaesthetic.

Without missing a beat, he listened before saying a little prayer and wishing me well. It may sound a little extreme, but it was another thing I wouldn't have to worry about and nor would my family, which gave me peace. However, I had no intention of meeting my maker and almost a year had passed since I had planned to climb Mount Snowden. Over Easter weekend, I did exactly that with my children, Michael and our dear friends Danny, an experienced mountaineer, Cheryl and their daughter Shelley. I climbed an actual mountain for the first time in my life and so had my children. It mattered to me that they knew to work hard, aim for the moon and that they should always dream big. If they had climbed a mountain, what else could they do?

During that weekend, a plan was hatched to make a really big statement to cancer, that I was in charge and I vowed to climb Ben Nevis, the biggest mountain in Britain. It meant I could draw a line in the sand that I was well and strong and had a future to look forward to. Michael vowed to walk beside me, as he always had. Friends asked if they could join us and I happily agreed. A date was set for June 14 2014, flights booked to Inverness, a mini bus and hotel booked in Fort William, at the foot of the mountain and a guide hired. I set about raising money for Breast Cancer Care and spent Fridays walking the Kent Downs with my friend Meagan and her dog Betsy in all weathers, to wear in my new walking boots and get some miles in my legs.

As we drove through the Scottish Highlands, from Inverness to Fort William, the Ben bore down ahead of us. It was snow capped, shrouded in thick grey cloud and its only inviting element was the challenge it offered. I got an early night, slept less than I would have liked, my phone pinging with messages from well wishers. The following morning, over £5000 had been pledged to Breast Cancer Care. I forced down breakfast into my nervous stomach and our party of 18 set off by taxi to the foot of the mountain. This meant so much to me. I had to make the summit.

It wasn't long before tears set in. My legs were fine but my emotions weren't. My friend Simon offered to carry my back pack but I refused. I was going to do this the same way as everyone else. No favours. No excuses. As we marched on, my friend Harry sensibly advised me to stop regularly and admire the scenery and not just look down at my boots, which I did. Two hours in, the sun came out and a rainbow sat below us. We were above the clouds and literally over the rainbow. The sky grew grey as we headed on and shirt sleeves were replaced with fleeces, jackets, gloves and hats, as our walking poles dug into packed snow. The Ben can be a beast and a bearer of all weathers. Our guide Chris promised that even if we just touched the summit and headed straight back down, he would get me there, which reassured me that months of training in the gym and on the hills would be worthwhile. He was as good as his word and we were able to get to the summit and stay a while to take photos and refuel and I hugged Michael before we made our descent. The climb down is hard on the knees, far harder than the 4413 feet climb up. My tears had gone though and I smiled all the way back to the base of the mountain. Simon was first at the bar of the Ben Nevis Inn and presented me with a pint of lager. Never before or since, have I downed a pint without stopping.

Relief overwhelmed us all a little as we headed back to our hotel in taxis. A quick change and we went down for dinner. I wrote a poem for everyone, titled *Lucky Chick*, about just how lucky I was to have the friendship of those around me at the table. I had also arranged for medals for everyone and laid both at their places at the dinner table. The following morning we headed home, none of us quite believing that we'd done it, some vowing to continue and conquer the three peaks challenge and others vowing never to step on a mountain again.

***

The following week, I was back in the chemo ward, having another dose of Herceptin fed into my arm. I didn't like being a patient, being vulnerable and as kind as the nursing staff were, I didn't like being in that room. Until that day. With just five visits left, the end was in sight. And thanks to the Ben, I was smiling.

As soon as Herceptin was finished, along with my visits to Pine Therapy for the best part of two long years, November reared and despite threats of being busy or on holiday on the day of my second mastectomy and bilateral reconstruction, Seema Seetharam attended at Queen Victoria Hospital, East Grinstead. She performed the mastectomy and plastic surgeon Simon set about the painstaking 10-hour operation to remove my temporary implant, move my stomach tissue to my chest and once again create two new breasts. As I lay hooked up to machines and drips in the high dependency unit, with observations every 10 minutes, my phone rang. I reached across to answer a call from Holly. Once again, I had fibbed to our children that I was having a minor hospital stay, nothing to worry about.

'Mum, I'm going to be late for school, the bus hasn't come,' she said. I smiled. I was dosed up on painkillers, with wires, tubes and drains all over my bed and her life was still normal and she was calling her mum. Surely a triumph. 'Don't worry darling, Dad is around today, I'll call him and get him to run you in,' which I did.

The surgery went smoothly and Simon appeared at my bedside the following day to check on me. Once again, he had done a wonderful job and apart from one more minor operation to create new nipples, his work with me was done. A truly brilliant medic and kind human, he remained true to his promise to be there for me and is the reason I will have peace of mind for life. My recovery was steady, with no complications.

I was referred to a new oncologist, Julia Hall, to arrange my ongoing drug treatment. Tamoxifen was replaced by an aromatase inhibitor, Exemestane, which I would need to take for up to 10 years to frighten off any lurking cancer. In order to further reduce risk, the following year I opted for an elective keyhole removal of both fallopian tubes and ovaries (bilateral salpingo oophrectomy) at Maidstone Hospital. An overnight stay and a week of recovery and I was back driving and getting on with my life.

After five years, Julia Hall closed my file, with an option to check in with her if I had any further worries. Now, I have an annual abdominal scan to check for further cancer cells and a bone scan every 18 months to check that Exemestane isn't reducing my bone density, a common side effect. I do everything I can, with weight bearing exercise and a nutrient rich diet to make sure that never happens. I'm out of the tunnel and so very grateful for every new day.

WHY FITTER STRONGER?

FITTER Stronger started as a naive desire to share the knowledge base I'd accumulated during my treatment: a positive mind-set, exercise and no-nonsense nutrition for a healthy mind and body, in a weekend fitness holiday for those coping with illness, injury and trauma, the like of which I couldn't find when I needed it most. With no health or fitness qualifications of my own, I pulled together a team of the very best nutritionists and fitness experts. The first of these holidays ran in September 2015. I then trained as a personal trainer, to take an active coaching role. Over time, it has organically developed into a series of programmes that operate in hospitals, schools, further education, private classes, one to one sessions, corporate events and as fitness holidays in the UK and South Africa. At the core of all of the Fitter Stronger programmes is the same principal - if you keep your mind and body strong, you can achieve so much more than you think possible.

***

Those nine damning words, 'There's nothing you can do to change your situation', uttered by my dismissive oncologist, as I quizzed him about the effect of drug treatment on my body, trying to make sense of how I would manage the two years ahead and the exercise and nutrition plan I would adopt to strengthen my body, became the catalyst for Fitter Stronger. I didn't want anyone else to feel that they had no control, however debilitating their situation.

Even on the toughest days during my treatment, I had no intention of surrendering to my diagnosis. I wanted to do all I could to support myself physically. Certainly, I couldn't change my diagnosis. Exhaustive tests had proven that my aggressive HER 2 positive breast cancer was not to be messed with. It had quietly set up home in my chest, giving no clue whatsoever. I felt healthy, well, and active and had no outward physical indicators. And it had got into my lymph nodes and was on the march. If it hadn't been detected by accident, during breast reduction surgery, my oncologist and I may well have been having a far more sinister conversation.

But I could certainly be the decision maker in how I handled it. I didn't want to succumb to two years of being a victim. I wanted to be proactive and do all I could to live as much of my life in that time as possible, for the good of my physical and mental health. I aimed for as much normality as I could achieve when my body allowed, not just a constant itinerary of blood tests, chemo, ultrasounds, MRIs, surgery and check-ups. I'm now sometimes asked to talk at medical conferences and I recall my oncologist's words and implore those in front of me to remember that they are addressing a human with feelings, a life of experiences and dreams ahead, to be positive always and to choose their words carefully.

I had two young children to fight for, a husband, a career that had enabled me to travel the world and have extraordinary adventures for 28 years, initially as a news journalist and then a feature writer, a busy social life. I had no intention of surrendering any more of this to cancer than was absolutely necessary. I would navigate this situation, control my fear and remain positive for my own sake and for those who depended on me.

***

Determined to find out as much as I could about supporting my body through treatment, I called Karen, a friend who'd had breast cancer two years earlier. Like me, she liked a healthy lifestyle and she gave me lots of information about the highs and lows and how to boost my immunity during different stages of treatment. I then scoured books and the internet for exercise and nutrition to support illness and was alarmed to find very little. I had hoped for an informative weekend retreat with targeted stress-busting exercise and nourishing food. Instead I found a plethora of meditative yoga breaks and boot camps but nothing for me. One failed spa trip led to further enquiries, all spas profusely apologising that their business insurance wouldn't cover a client with breast cancer - the tide has turned a little here now and you are less likely to be turned away. My chemo nurses and oncologist encouraged me to eat whatever I liked to keep my energy up, avoiding uncooked fish and unpasteurised dairy. I chose to avoid processed food, fat and sugar - the devil incarnate duo for cancer, supporting cancer cell growth - downloaded whole food recipes, inflicted wholegrain rice and lentil burger experiments on my bewildered family, overhauled my kitchen cupboards, blended nutrient rich smoothies, researched the effects of vitamins and minerals, how best to support my metabolism and ensured there was sufficient calcium in my diet to keep my bones dense, as bone thinning was a common side effect of the drugs I was taking.

***

Towards the end of my drug treatment, in the autumn of 2014, just before my second mastectomy and reconstruction surgery, I took a job as arts and culture editor at *Saga Magazine*. As a news and features writer for almost three decades, I had walked all the red carpets I wanted to walk. I'd taken to the sky with rock stars in helicopters, flown to Milan for lunch, to New York for opening nights on Broadway, covered all kinds of acrimony, wars, royal stories, stayed in the smartest hotels and seen the very best and very worst of humanity. It was my dream job and the only career I'd ever wanted from childhood but I had spent the previous two years evaluating what mattered to me most. Now I wanted more time to hug those I loved. This new nine to five job fitted in with family life. I spent my days commissioning writers to create copy on new books, music, theatre, television and the arts. I was part of a small team, based in Sandgate, near Folkestone. There were walks by the sea with colleagues at lunchtime and weekends and evenings off. My 50-minute commute meant I had time to think through my first Fitter Stronger wellness break for those coping with illness, injury or trauma. The more I thought about it, the more I wanted to do it.

***

I created a website, registered my Fitter Stronger business at Companies House and met up with Paul, a travel industry friend whose worldwide properties I had stayed in many times as a writer, who introduced me to the team at Chewton Glen Hotel and Spa in Hampshire, near the New Forest. A meeting was arranged with the hotel's commercial director Leigh Jenkins in April 2015, who heard my pitch and despite my having no previous track record in hospitality, very kindly agreed to house my first Fitter Stronger Retreat and host a press weekend in September to launch it. I set about putting a team together. I needed someone who had walked a difficult line with their own health and would motivate others. As a journalist I had interviewed Olympic rower James Cracknell as an elite athlete and after his brain injury, following a near fatal collision with a fuel truck, while cycling Route 66 across America. James had told me that he used exercise as his coping mechanism for his recovery and that the improvements in his strength and coordination, of his own making, encouraged him to persevere with rehab and rebuild his life. He went on to complete the London marathon in two hours, 50 minutes and the Yukon Arctic Ultra – the coldest race on earth, in the Canadian Yukon Mountains. I contacted him, we met in London and he agreed to be my motivational speaker. I told James I needed a nutritionist, who would deliver a potentially dull subject in a no-nonsense way and hold the interest of my guests and James referred me to his own nutritionist, Fred Wadhurst, whose wide ranging knowledge you will find in chapter 14 of this book. Fred and I met, agreed on the same nutrition principles and he agreed to join my fledgling team.

My fitness squad, Simon Jones and Mitch Sherwood, had both trained me during my illness and since. Simon had climbed Ben Nevis with me. They had the right mix of knowledge, grit and comedy, to make exercise fun, achievable and targeted to whoever stood in front of them and kindly agreed to get involved.

I'd done a lot of my thinking in woodland, near my house. Being in nature, putting one foot in front of the other, improved my clarity of thought, suppressed rising cortisol on stressful days, and was a joy on good days, as I watched the seasons change. During my illness, it was always easier to talk to friends more freely while facing forwards, when we didn't see each other's face or body language, which we do when walking. I wanted to include a hike at my retreat and hired guide Scott Smith, a former paratrooper. Now an international mountain guide, we met at a CrossFit gym, where we both trained and he agreed to lead my guests through the New Forest.

With my team complete and a beautiful venue, I called in favours from colleagues, to attend a press launch on the first weekend of September 2015, write wonderful things to promote my first Fitter Stronger Retreat at Chewton Glen and give me honest feedback.

***

During a weekend trip to my local gym, while working for *Saga Magazine*, I saw an advert in reception, for a part-time gym instructor, offering to train the successful applicant on site as a level 2 gym instructor and duty manager. The gym was very much still my happy place. I attended my local gym and a CrossFit gym to concentrate on weight lifting to improve my bone density. I loved seeing what my body was capable of and became fascinated by the process of recovery following surgery or drug therapy. I'd already discovered that exercise and good nutrition had made me feel physically and mentally stronger, offering clarity during difficult decision making and enabling me to climb Britain's biggest two mountains between trips wired to drips on the chemo ward. On the way home from the CrossFit gym, after a particularly exhilarating workout, I stopped the car on the motorway hard shoulder. I phoned my local gym and asked if I could apply. I was 47 years-old. When I thought of gym instructors, I pictured ripped, fresh faced 20-somethings. Gym instructors didn't look like me, a CrossFit keen, weight lifting, running, dancing 40-something. I was told to send in my CV, that interviews would be held in three days time and they would be in touch. There were three applicants and I didn't hold out much hope. I had no expertise to offer, just lots of enthusiasm. I had a job and it was fine if it didn't work out. I could not have been more shocked or delighted when I was told I'd got the position and given my gym uniform. A few days later, after a year at *Saga Magazine*, I handed in my notice. At my leaving lunch, I was handed a bag of outdoor kit including a camel bladder and head torch, in case I should embark on any new expeditions and some vouchers for smart new stationary for my Fitter Stronger home office. I shared hugs with colleagues before clearing my desk and heading to my car, turning my back on journalism, a decision I could never have predicted, to start a new career in the health and fitness industry in my late 40s.

***

During my illness I did a lot of thinking. If I survived cancer, I was probably half way through my life. I decided from then on that if anything or anyone kept me awake at night, I would remove them from my life. I also decided to stop procrastinating and have lots more adventures. My rationale with every new project thenceforth became the same — what's the worst that could happen? I reasoned that if no one took me seriously as a fitness instructor or Fitter Stronger retreats were empty, I could go back to writing as a freelance journalist. One positive to take from my cancer experience was that I was wasting no more time. Life was short and to be cherished. I had altered the direction of my life and re-set my boundaries.

I was off to a good start. I was about to start a new part-time job as a trainee fitness instructor, sharing my passion for exercise, launch a new business and host a well-being retreat, where I could share the knowledge base I built up to navigate my illness and recovery, with others whose health had been compromised.

***

The following week, wearing my new standard issue gym uniform of black Life Fitness polo shirt and hoodie, with my black lycra leggings and trainers, I started my training as a gym instructor and duty manager, with weekly tutorials and lots of homework on how to safely deliver exercise in a gym, utilising all the equipment and understanding health and safety protocols. Aside from the gym manager, the rest of the gym team were less than half my age, welcoming and friendly. During quieter night shifts at Meopham Fitness Centre, my fellow duty manager and friend James, who had a sports science degree, would patiently test me before my exams, after which I was able to coach gym clients and run small classes.

My first client was Mary Jenner, a 64 year-old sprightly lady, with neat, curly blonde hair, who approached me one evening, explaining she needed to increase mobility following knee surgery. I booked her in and arranged to meet her the following day. After completing a standard gym health Q&A form, we moved to the treadmill, where she walked, gradually increasing her speed, as she told me that she was a Masters GB team badminton athlete and needed to be in the strongest possible position for the next World Championship, in Sweden, three months later. She had team training but wanted to top this up. Masters athletes aren't sponsored in Britain to the same extent as her opponents from Russia and China, so she paid for her additional gym membership herself. On alternate years, the World Masters and European Masters championships took place and two years ago, in the last World Championships, she had won a silver medal. This time she wanted to leave with a gold medal. No pressure then.

I explained that I wasn't a personal trainer and there were others better qualified but she insisted on working with me and my gym manager allowed it. We met every week, increased her leg and upper body power, creating strength in the muscles that would support her weaknesses, built her core and developed mobility through her back. She was my kind of woman. She loved a goal, was prepared to work for it and saw obstacles to climb, rather than things that would block her path. Mary's World Championship would take place on the same weekend as my Fitter Stronger press launch.

***

As my September retreat launch grew closer, the final details were signed off. The meals had been agreed with the hotel and their nutritional content added to each page of the menus. I'd had meetings with each of my recently assembled team to discuss their contribution and how and when it would be delivered and given them all team hoodies to wear. My press photographer friend Jonathan agreed to attend and take photos that he would supply to each of the publications, which included *Daily Mail Health, Daily Mail Weekend magazine, GQ, Men's Health, Telegraph, Sunday Express, Sunday Mirror* and *Good Spa Magazine*.

After a reception and welcome drinks and snacks, everyone loved settling into their luxurious Chewton Glen bedrooms before embarking on their first exercise session with Simon and Mitch. Journalist Ross Edgley, now best known for swimming round Great Britain, kept a little energy in his tank and challenged James Cracknell to a rowing session in the hotel gym. Ross is a good deal shorter than James, whose long limbs and three Olympic gold medals soon left Ross gasping but grateful for his rowing lesson. James spent the afternoon giving an honest account of his story, leading up to and recovering from his brain injury, as he motivated my press guests and charmed each journalist in turn through their interviews, before they enjoyed a delicious but healthy feast in the hotel restaurant. The following day, after more exercise, Fred's informative nutrition talk and Scott's hike through the New Forest, my guests enjoyed one more evening at Chewton Glen, before my Fitter Stronger Retreat press launch came to an end. As they departed after breakfast on Sunday morning, new friends made and numbers swapped between them, their faces were smiling and their feedback was positive. My team had been amazing, supportive and dedicated, as had the Chewton Glen staff. I could not have wished for a better outcome for this fledgling venture, as I made my way home on Sunday, from Hampshire to Kent.

***

The following evening, I was working at the leisure centre, when Mary arrived, wearing her GB team tracksuit. She had flown home from Sweden the previous night. I had tried to follow her progress online during my retreat launch in Hampshire but had failed to find the World Championship updates. Mary said nothing, but slowly unzipped her GB team tracksuit top. Beneath it, she proudly wore a gold medal, hanging on a red ribbon. I ran round the desk and hugged her. I could not have been more proud of her. She trained consistently and got her reward. She was World Champion. She was everything I wanted professionally - a client who had a weakness, set a goal and was determined to overcome and achieve it with no excuses. Mary inspired me every time I worked with her. She handed me a box containing a white mug bearing the Swedish flag, which still sits proudly on a shelf in my office and card bearing the greatest compliment of all. She wrote that I had not only made her physically stronger, I had given her confidence and taught her to believe in herself. What a great start.

**

I followed my level 2 gym instructor qualification with a level 3 personal trainer qualification in April 2016, deepening my knowledge about delivering exercise, anatomy and physiology and nutrition and left Meopham gym shortly afterwards to become a self-employed personal trainer. This meant I could spend more time with individual clients, developing their goals over a period of time, which brought new, interesting challenges. In my first year, I worked with ex-military servicemen who wanted to maintain their fitness, a newly accepted Sandhurst trainee army officer who wanted to prepare for what lay ahead, anti-terrorism and royal protection squad Metropolitan Police officers who needed to prepare for their beep tests, pregnant and post pregnancy women and those ladies who wanted to shed pounds to get into their little black dresses.

**

The invited press had written many column inches of praise about Fitter Stronger Retreat, with the *Telegraph* naming it as the best fitness holiday in the UK and Fitter Stronger Retreat was now advertised to the paying public for the first time. The first retreat ran at Chewton Glen in May 2016 and I'll never forget it, for all the right reasons. My team reunited, save for Fred who was unavailable but connected me with Helene Patounas, the nutritionist for all of the Formula One racing teams, who agreed to step in, was a great new asset and has become a dear friend.

My clients included two ladies and a gentleman with head injuries of varying severity. Their exercise programmes were carefully programmed and personal trainer and Pilate's instructor Simon Jones, added a Pilates session. All of the guests were fascinated by James and his recovery. James joined our guests for dinner before leaving and wishing me well. The following day, Scott designed the hike in the New Forest estimating how long each client would be able to walk and suitable points where they could stop and be returned to the hotel by one of the team. One of our guests, John, had amused us all over dinner with his repetitive storytelling and great charm. However, his wife Suzie was nervous about her husband exercising, as previous exertion had lead to epileptic fits. To our surprise and their delight, he completed the two-hour hike, along with all the guests, without incident. As we all climbed back into Scott's Land Rover to return to the hotel, John called me over, with tears in his eyes, and said 'Thank you, for everything.' His wife Suzie explained that the hike had given them both confidence. If he could do this, perhaps they could leave their house more often.

***

Annual retreats continued to run at Chewton Glen, alongside more at a second venue, Brandshatch Place Hotel and Spa. Each time, I received cards and notes from happy clients, explaining that the Fitter Stronger Retreat programme of exercise, nutrition and motivation gave them the resilience to cope with their individual situations, which were wide ranging, from strokes, cancer and brain injury to bereavement and loneliness.

I thought of my children and how difficult it had been for them to come to terms with their mum getting cancer, how hurt and scared they had been, however much I reassured them. Even now, if they hear of a cancer death, they will just check in with me that I'm really OK. I started to think that if we could make an impact with adults, it would be very satisfying to help young people who, when beset by trauma, don't have the years behind them and emotional intelligence to process their situation.

In 2018, I set about creating a free Fitter Stronger day, for young people aged 11 to 18, who were struggling with illness, injury or trauma. I gathered a team around me, including Simon from my adult retreats, who would lead a group of my personal trainer and PE teacher friends, to encourage and cajole teens through a fitness session. Instructors Gemma and Nora, who had coached me through my personal training course, lead an interactive nutrition session. My PE teacher friend Tommy took a street dance class and I invited two motivational speakers, Greig Trout from The Kindness Project – introduced to me by his sister-in-law – my nutritionist friend Helene Patounas and Javid Abdelmoneim, a hospital A&E doctor who volunteers for charity Medicins Sans Frontieres, who I'd heard speak at an event Helene had invited me to. They were all supported by my paramedic friend Alan and his A&E sister wife Liz and a group of my teacher and police friends who would be my eyes and a pair of listening ears for any young people who were struggling with any aspect of the day, which would end with a disco. Everyone had DBS checks and would be giving up their Sunday for free. I also invited along BBC News to cover the event, to highlight how children's mental and physical health needed supporting, with as much freely available exercise as possible, as a coping mechanism for illness, injury and trauma.

Schools, colleges and youth groups advertised the event and 60 young people attended. Their situations varied from leukaemia, to domestic strife, anxiety and depression, some extremely reluctant to step through the door, cajoled by my wonderful, kind team, who were rewarded at the end of the day with lots of happy young faces. I spoke to each child as they left with their parent or carer and asked them if anything changed in their life as a direct result of the day, could they let me know. The brilliant thing about working with young people is that they don't mince their words. One 14 year-old girl, Sarah, who had arrived alone, incredibly shy, held her head up, looked at her astonished mum, and told her, 'I learned today that I can achieve anything I want to.' Another girl, Amelia, had arrived with leukaemia and was regularly at hospital for blood transfusions. She took part in every activity and thanked me, saying, 'Today, for the first time in ages I feel normal. I could do everything and had such a lovely time.'

The BBC broadcast two films about the event the following day, a shorter one at lunchtime and another in their evening programme. My phone, social media and email received dozens of enquiries for a repeat event. The following day, I was walking in the woods with my friend Rebecca and insisted it had been a one-off event and that I couldn't call in lots more favours. She suggested that instead of running it in a hotel and asking young people to come to me, I could go to those young people and run it in schools.

I went home, emailed the schools who had sent children along to the Brandshatch event, explained how well they had acquitted themselves and what they had learned and offered to come into school if this was of interest. All of those teachers replied within the hour. I put a team together to go into schools, and my Recharge programme, of exercise, nutrition and motivation for young people, charging a nominal fee, was born. In three years, we have worked with over 3000 vulnerable young people in schools, colleges, youth groups, apprenticeship schemes and charities. The stories of what those young people have gone on to achieve have been heart warming. I'll get an email, or a direct social media message or best of all, I'll get stopped in the street with a, 'Do you remember me, Miss? I'm still eating properly, I passed my exams and I'm at college now. Thanks Miss.'

Young people get a bad press but I have heard so many good things about what they are doing in their communities; setting up food banks, raising funds for local charities, volunteering with dementia patients, being carers to their sick parents, that I wanted their quiet selflessness to be recognised. In 2019 I created the Recharge Awards, which now runs annually at Brandshatch Place Hotel & Spa, sponsored by shirt makers, Hilditch & Key. The categories range from art, sport and music to community, kindness, communication, innovation and there is one adult award, educator of the year, for someone who has gone out of their way to help a young person realise their goal. My Recharge team and sponsor decide the shortlist and winners, who are all filmed, so they get to tell their own story. Each time, there isn't a dry eye in the house and everyone leaves safe in the knowledge that our next generation is good and kind and generous.

***

I often have clients referred to me by doctors, chiropractors and osteopaths, to improve their mobility and was keen to work closely with hospitals. Last year, I started my free Revive initiative, with Queen Mary's Hospital, Sidcup and Queen Victoria Hospital, East Grinstead, to work with cancer patients, getting them fit before and after treatment. They are all so much happier knowing that they can be proactive by empowering their bodies, with exercise and nutrition, in similar ways that I used when I was ill, and I'm happy to be working with the NHS to offer this prehab and rehab pathway.

***

As a journalist, my favourite assignment was covering Nelson Mandela's election, in South Africa. I spent six glorious weeks there and fell in love with the landscape, the wildlife and made many friends. I found every tenuous excuse I could over my following years as a journalist to return and write further features about tourism or conservation. Most of all, I loved spending hours on safari, either in a vehicle or on foot on non predator land. Nothing calmed me more than being among nature and wildlife and I learned so much from those animals about survival, working as a team and trust. I've visited with my husband and children and it's still my favourite home away from home. My dear friend Will Fowlds, renowned wildlife vet and part owner of Amakhala Game Reserve in the Eastern Cape, encouraged me to consider setting up a retreat at his country house, Leeuwenbosch. I was sceptical about whether people would want to combine exercise and nutrition with safari but we put Fitter Stronger Goes Wild together and I had sold all the places in less than two weeks. The first Fitter Stronger Goes Wild event ran in November 2019. Along with exercise and nutrition, guests assist Will with a low risk animal procedure in the bush while learning about conservation, we visit the Born Free big cat sanctuary, enjoy braai dinners with music and dancing, horse riding, a history lesson from South African story teller Rob Caskie, game drives, a walking safari and river cruise. Guests are encouraged to put their phones and cameras down and be in the moment with nature, appreciating their environment. All of our guests comment on how relaxed they felt on departure, despite exercising every day, and how their environment had made them reconsider the pace and direction of their lives. Nature nurtures.

***

I feel extremely lucky to be able to do a job I love with so many different, rewarding, interesting arms; working with individuals in personal training or with Revive cancer patients, with groups on my fitness holidays and at classes and with young people. At the core of all I do, the message is the same. Keep your mind and body strong and you are unstoppable.

THIS IS ME

WHEN we are facing a change in our lives, it can seem overwhelming, disturbing, all consuming. Consultant psychiatrist Phil Hopley explained earlier that it is our previous life experience that will determine our reaction to change. Our brain calculates whether we stay rooted to the spot, burying our head in the sand, tackle that change head on or run from it.

As a young woman, when I was facing a situation that I found uncomfortable, a bad boyfriend choice or toxic work environment, I'd run rather than face confrontation: change jobs, rent a new flat in a new area... I hadn't been taught how to stand my ground and be heard and would always fear the consequences of speaking up. My mindset has very much altered as I've got older.

During my illness, I made a decision not to waste another day and entertain nothing in my life that would keep me awake at night. I no longer accommodate the elephant in the room. If something needs to be said, politely, I'll say it. More often than not, this means the other person and I may agree to disagree, harbour no ill feeling and maintain a mutual respect. If we can't do this, that person no longer has a place in my life and will not receive so much as a backward glance.

Of course there are times when change is enforced upon us, like the loss of someone we love and the grief process needs to run its full course and we must seek help here if necessary, in order to move forwards.

It's easy to blame our losses and previous experience for our current situation. I love the saying, *If you always do what you've always done, you'll always get what you've always got*. If we want to make changes to improve our situation, it doesn't matter where we start. All that matters is where we finish. Deciding to make change takes courage but the rewards are always worth it. As soon as I realised this, my life became richer, more adventurous, more fun. If I have one regret it is that I wish I'd been braver sooner.

***

I grew up in Deptford, south east London, in the 70s, before it was trendy. My mum would always give Lewisham, five miles down the road, as her address, because she thought it sounded smarter, though it really wasn't. Letters invariably arrived with Lewisham crossed out by the Post Office and Deptford added, much to her annoyance.

My father, mother, two younger sisters and I relocated from Pinner, Middlesex, when I was aged two as my father thought it was an up and coming area. Our detached house sat between a doctor's surgery to our right, which was regularly raided for drugs by local addicts, flats to our left and opposite a church.

My father commuted to his job as an accounts clerk at the old Covent Garden Market. He insisted we went to the church opposite our house on Sundays and the vicar was a regular for Sunday lunch, when our wooden dining table would be adorned with a lace tablecloth and candelabra. Sometimes my father and I would draw together and I have memories of us visiting the National Gallery in London, wearing my smart coat for best, leaving my two younger sisters at home with my mother and wandering around the huge rooms of paintings.

On one occasion, we flew to Amsterdam for the weekend, walking round the flower markets and trying on clogs. I later discovered he hadn't told my mother where we were. In the absence of email or mobile phones, she was worried and furious when we returned.

When I was aged nine, their relationship deteriorated and my father became violent towards my mother. He drank a lot of Johnnie Walker Red Label whisky and puffed constantly on Dunhill cigarettes. To keep my sisters and I safe at night, my mother would sleep with us beneath blue cellular blankets in the living room, while he stayed in their bedroom. Sometimes the plan would fail and he would appear and turn the record player on loud. A row would ensue to the soundtrack of Tina Charles' *I Love to Love* or any of the Carpenters' back catalogue, and he'd throw whatever was at hand at my mother, while we ducked, before he walked away. My most disturbing memory is watching my father, who had become addicted to a cocktail of hallucinogenic drugs, try to push my mother along the landing and down the stairs, as I clung to his back and begged him to stop, which he eventually did.

One day, our mother announced she was leaving and that that I was in charge. I was 10. My sisters were aged seven and four. And she left to stay with her mother. She was gone just a few days but it seemed forever. We didn't go to school and my father, too intoxicated to work, would put me on the phone to ask her to return, which she eventually did.

When my mother couldn't face being at home with her unpredictable and violent husband, a bag was hastily packed and we all made a temporary move to a friend's house or a women's refuge centre. Keen to maintain her pride, my mother would insist my sisters and I wore our smartest coats and I always pushed my small teddy bear in my bag, so I could bury my face in his soft, comforting tummy when I couldn't sleep.

And so it went on. Weeks turned into months and this was our normal. Sometimes school, sometimes not. Sometimes violence, sometimes not. Sometimes sleeping at home, sometimes not. An attempt to find a permanent new home from the council fell on deaf ears, as my mother had a home and an income from my father, in the unenlightened 70s and so she wasn't eligible.

One night, while we were staying with a friend of my mother's and her two daughters, the phone rang for my mother, who had told our long suffering neighbours where we were. When she replaced the receiver, I asked who it was and she calmly and unemotionally told me my father had committed suicide and was dead. She was visibly relieved. He had hung himself from a rope, on our stair banisters. Our neighbour had gone to check on him, found his body, cut him down and attempted to resuscitate him but it was futile.

***

I later learned that my father had been embezzling money at his work place to fund his drug habit. He faced a court hearing the day he committed suicide and couldn't face a prison sentence, after spending much of his early life in Borstal youth detention centre. He had grown up angry, not knowing his own father and spent much of his young life in a care home, after my grandmother became a single mother. He had joined the merchant navy when he met my Portuguese mother and they started a new life together in England.

***

I was devastated. He had created chaos, acted viciously, violently and selfishly, heaping fear and uncertainty on his family but he didn't explain or apologise or say goodbye. It hadn't happened for a long time but there would be no more drawing together or trips to the National Gallery. That bit of good in him definitely wasn't coming back now. I said nothing but ran to the bathroom and sobbed quietly until there were no tears left. When my mother asked why I'd been crying, I wiped my face and lied that I was fine.

***

A few days later, we returned to our house. The house had been tidied but the rope marks on the white gloss paint work, where my father had hung, were still there. I was wounded, empty, angry, upset, confused. If I asked questions, these were met with my mother's anger, so I quickly learned not to. I was 10 years-old and bewildered. I wanted answers, reasons, a rationale, a plan for the future but none were forthcoming. My mother told me a funeral was no place for children so my sisters and I stayed away while my father was buried at Grove Park Cemetery.

***

I visited my father's grave some years later, alone, aged 14. As I got off the bus, the sky was as grey and heavy as my heart as I walked around until I found him. When I found his white headstone, there were no tears. I stood for a while. I said goodbye. And I didn't return.

***

Six months after my father died, I joined Bonus Pastor Secondary School in Downham, Kent, at the very arse end of the garden of England. I had attended a Church of England primary school and been christened into the Church of England, at my father's behest. Following his death, my mother, a non practising Roman Catholic, insisted that her children would attend a school linked to her faith. At the meeting with the headmaster Mr Milne, a kind, rotund Irishman, he asked me if I could recite the Hail Mary. I shifted awkwardly in my chair and told him I didn't know it. He then asked me if I could tell him each of the Stations of the Cross. Again, I hung my head and shook it slowly. Not only did I not know these, I knew nothing whatsoever about Catholicism. Finally, Mr Milne said, 'Well Paula, have you heard of St Jude?' Once more I shook my head. He smiled and told me, 'Well you go away and pray to St Jude and we'll see what we can do.' St Jude is the patron saint of lost causes.

***

In a black blazer, A-line grey skirt and white socks, I embarked on a solo 45-minute two-bus journey to my new school. I mumbled through each assembly until I finally learned the words and appropriate actions to all the Catholic prayers. A free school lunch meant joining a daily queue to collect the required pink ticket for pie and mash and pink sponge with pink custard, before more lessons and the bus home, where tension hung in the air like a heavy grey cloud. My mother took a job in the canteen at a local college to pay the bills, was almost constantly grumpy, reminding my sisters and I how hard she worked and that this isn't what she was promised when she met my father in Madeira.

My father had bought me a cassette player the previous September for my birthday and two cassettes, *Trouble* by Sailor and *Laughter in the Rain* by Neil Sedaka. I played these a lot and listened to my little orange radio late into the night on headphones, loving to escape into music. When the atmosphere grew too cold at home, I'd visit our neighbours, Bill and Vi and their teenage daughter, Julie. Vi would invariably welcome me into their flat with a slice of warm bread pudding with sugar on top and we'd chat until I was called home.

At school, I made a small group of lovely friends and I lived for three lessons - swimming, art and English. Our swimming lessons meant a class trip each week to Crystal Palace pool. I was strong and encouraged to swim distances. Five hundred metres? A mile? Yes please. I'd concentrate on my breathing. I loved how my muscles relaxed and how calm I felt afterwards. I slept so much better after swimming too, as dopamine coursed through my veins, untying the knots in my stomach and lowering my blood pressure.

In art, I'd lose myself in my creativity and discovered it was one of the few things I was good at. Our art teacher, Mr Connolly, wore a tweed suit and had a beard, moustache and glasses. Nothing exceptional there but his lessons were imaginative. He'd play *Lucy in the Sky With Diamonds* by the Beatles and ask us to paint whatever vision was stirred in our minds. He took us to the National Gallery and we walked past the paintings I'd viewed with my father when I was younger, until we stopped in front of Titian's glorious *Bacchus and Ariadne*. I loved the party that was going down in that painting, which tells the story of a young woman dumped by her boyfriend, when a new guy rocks up and tells her, stick with me and I'll show you the stars. I thought it was fantastic. It symbolised a crossroads. Go left and there was certain misery. Turn right and there was promise of an adventure. It spelled hope to me, 500 years after it was painted. I love it still. We don't have to choose misery. If we are brave enough to accept change, there is the opportunity for new beginnings.

The only other subject that held my interest at school was English. I loved escaping into books, immersing myself in the characters I read about, their environments, their lives. And I loved to write. Whatever the brief, I loved every aspect of the research, the expression, the language. Vi, our next door neighbour always had a copy of *The Sun* newspaper and I'd read it cover to cover, devouring the stories of lives a world away from mine. I watched the news, too and was fascinated by the BBC's Africa correspondent Michael Buerk and his tales of politics, cultures I didn't know and canoeing down the Zambezi River. Aged 14, I decided I would become a newspaper journalist, reasoning that this seemed to be a great way to travel and see the world. I had no idea if this plan would ever work but I knew two things: I didn't want my mother's joyless life and I sure as hell didn't want my father's life either.

***

In the summer holidays, just before my 16th birthday, I wrote to John Blake, the then editor of *Bizarre*, the pop music column in *The Sun*. I told him I liked music and I wanted to be a journalist and asked if I could come and see his newspaper. When the typed envelope with my name on it and a red *Sun* stamp dropped through my letter box a week later, I carefully peeled it open, to reveal an invitation from John Blake to call and arrange a day to visit Fleet Street. By now, I had a Saturday job in Littlewoods in Lewisham High Street and saved up my wages to pay for a smart outfit and my train fare. I loved walking through the office to the clatter of typewriters and trill of telephones. John's desk was on the far side of a cluster of four tables and he patiently sat me down and asked me why I wanted to work in newspapers and I told him I wanted to see the world. He asked me about the music I liked and I was shown around the office, to the news and subs desks and given proofs of the following day's pages to read. In an age before social media and mobile phones, I loved being in this fast moving, noisy environment, where you were first to hear a news story breaking that could shift the mood of the nation and drank it all in. John asked if I'd like to try a different newspaper the following week. When I eagerly agreed that I would, he called Peter Holt, who allowed me to spend the day with him on *Ad Lib*, the pop music page of the *Evening Standard*. Peter sent me the following week to Daniela Soave at *Record Mirror* to try magazines and I was sold. I loved that music journalists got to hang out with pop stars, visit them in their homes, overseas and were paid to see them in concert. What teenager wouldn't want that job? I certainly absolutely did.

***

At school, I met my careers teacher who dismissed any notion of journalism and aspiration. Uninspired, I endured one year of Sixth Form and left to get a job as a contracts clerk at film company EMI. I loved working in Wardour Street, in the heart of the film industry. I met EMI's international distributors, one of whom offered to show me around Bangkok, so I earned my flight and took my first foreign holiday to Thailand and flew onto Singapore. I soaked up every assault on my senses.

***

Two years later, I took my next job, still in the contracts office, at satellite TV station Super Channel, in Rathbone Place, near Oxford Street. When my boss left and asked me to join him at Virgin Records, on Harrow Road, in west London, I agreed. I learned to drive and bought my first car. As a steady stream of albums and gig tickets landed on my desk, my interest in pop music was stronger than ever but I still needed to find a way to do the job I really wanted, as a journalist.

***

I started volunteering for a hospital radio station at Guys Hospital. With no experience whatsoever and all the charm I could muster, I hosted a chat show and interviewed everyone from John Hurt to Bobby Womack. The late Peter Young, a

DJ at Capital Radio, was one of my guests. His producer was leaving and he asked if I would help him on his Sunday Evening Show, which I eagerly did.

***

At the hospital radio station, I invited Piers Morgan, then editor of *The Sun's Bizarre* pop column to review some new records I'd been sent. I mentioned to him that I'd wanted to be a journalist but now worked at Virgin Records and Capital Radio. Piers asked if I could write and if I'd like to come and try a shift on his column at *The Sun*. I took a day's leave from Virgin Records and headed to the newspaper's offices which were now in Wapping, the following week, nervous and excited.

Piers was on holiday and the column was being edited by his deputy, Peter Willis. Peter, stuck with an entirely untrained journalist on his desk, asked me to follow up a tip about the rock band Simple Minds, who had split with their management. He told me the name of their recording studio and asked me to find out why. I called the studio and asked to speak to lead singer Jim Kerr. The receptionist asked who was calling. I told her it was Paula Kerr. Assuming it was one of the Scot singer's family, she put me straight through. The musician politely explained his side of the story and I then rang his former manager, who spent the next 30 seconds shouting expletives down the phone, threatened to complain about me to then *Sun* editor Kelvin McKenzie and assured me I'd never work in Fleet Street again. I kept my head down when McKenzie walked through the office, certain he would hunt me down and throw me out. He didn't, of course. Instead, he walked over to the subs desk to review the headlines. There had been an oil slick off the south coast, devastating the sea bird population in the area. The chief sub editor had written a convoluted headline about the death of cormorants. 'What the 'ell's this?' barked McKenzie. Change it. Turn it into, 'Is this the last shag in Britain?' to riotous laughter from the rest of the newsroom.

The next day, my first story was published and I was offered more shifts at *The Sun*. I handed in my notice at Virgin Records and didn't return and left home to share a house with my school friend, Jacqui. I took all the newspaper shifts I was offered, mostly living on my wits, a bit of common sense, the ability to string a few words together coherently and type, which I'd learned at school. The more bylines I earned, the more work I was offered on other newspapers, including the *Daily Mail*, which operated a huge showbiz desk, with theatre writer Jack Tinker, film critic Shaun Usher and columnist Baz Bamigboye.

When the Gulf War began in August 1990, the public's appetite for show business news, that you could argue was rarely in the public interest, dried up overnight, as British soldiers were deployed to the Middle East. It was time to train as a news journalist, become Michael Buerk or a version of him and learn how to tell stories that were properly newsworthy.

***

I headed out of London, to the Bucks Free Press, who employed me and offered to send me to a journalism college, in Hastings, East Sussex. Usually hacks cut their teeth on local newspapers and then move on to national titles. My journey was unorthodox but necessary if I was going to be taken seriously as a news journalist. In the following six months, sharing a house with four other trainees, I learned shorthand, how to be a court reporter without getting on the wrong side of the law, that typing didn't count, no matter how fast you did it if you weren't using all 10 digits (I used eight, still do) and that if you really want to waste two hours of your life in your 20s, you should join a parish council meeting.

Before the ink was dry on my pass certificate, I was back in my car and sat in front of news editor, John McShane, at the *Sunday Mirror.* He eyed me and my lack of news experience warily. But to his credit, he gave me a chance to work my first news shift, on a Saturday. This was when he would try out regional news reporters who fancied their chances on a national newspaper. What followed was mostly lots of McShane losing his temper with the newbies, following his own frequent dressing down by *Mirror* proprietor, the late Robert Maxwell.

My upbringing was finally proving to be useful. No amount of questioning or barracking from McShane was going to faze me. I had seen far worse and he neither intimidated nor scared me. My first day began with a phone call before I got to the office, sending me to Paddington Station, where a black cab driver had been attacked by his fare. After speaking to police and witnesses, I headed to A&E at Queen Mary's Hospital and waited for further news. A weary doctor, who looked as though he had been working all night and probably had, came to tell me the cab driver had been fatally wounded, that they did all they could to revive him but he hadn't pulled through and was dead. He spoke softly and was devastated. So this was what news reporting felt like? It was a world away from film premieres, red carpets, interviews with actors in sumptuous hotel suites. This was cruel and brutal and absolutely every reason I ever wanted to be a journalist. I wanted to scream about injustice to the largest possible audience and be trusted to tell those stories. Weekend shifts at the *Sunday Mirror* were soon added to weekday shifts and more work followed at the *Daily Mail, Daily Express, Daily Star* and *Evening Standard.*

I moved into a new, tiny flat, opposite Kings Cross Station, surrounded by pimps and drug dealers, but, crucially, just a 10-minute drive to the *Express* building on Blackfriars Bridge. Living virtually above the shop guaranteed me heaps of work and with it, lots of experience. At my busiest, on weekdays I'd work for the *Daily Express* in Blackfriars by day and head across to Kensington to write for the *Evening Standard* by night, then work at the *Sunday Mirror* on Saturdays. By Saturday evening, I was so tired I could barely write my own name but I loved every minute of covering news stories as they were breaking, the camaraderie among my colleagues, travelling around the country and overseas. I never once had a legal case against me, despite securing the headlines and always parted company with those I interviewed with a handshake, whatever the situation.

***

The *Daily Express* building had its own bar and I was fascinated by the life of its chief foreign correspondent, Daniel McGrory. We were introduced and I listened intently one evening to his plans to cover the Balkan War. I had covered all kinds of news stories but a war would mean a real test of skill and nerve. I was ready for it but needed a commission. A friend suggested I contact BBC Radio 1 DJ Simon Bates, who was keen to cover the war in former Yugoslavia, where British soldiers were deployed as part of the UNHCR peacekeeping force, in some way on his morning programme. I had arranged to cover the work of Feed the Children with *Daily Mail* journalist David Williams and would travel around Croatia and Bosnia with the charity's aid worker Gordon Bacon, a former Durham police officer. Simon and I met and he equipped me with a broadcast quality tape recorder. Danny, who would be reporting in Sarajevo, told me how to become embedded with the army who would safely escort us to avoid sniper fire and I set off. The war between Serbs, Croats and Muslims was at its worst as night fell. British soldiers were powerless to intervene and had the job of collecting bodies when gunfire ceased. One night, as gunfire raged around us, at a British army base near Vitez, a soldier told me how he'd seen a mother and daughter run out of their house hand in hand when a grenade was thrown through their window and both were felled by sniper fire. When he went to collect their bodies, they were still holding hands.

I visited a hospital in Tuzla to help deliver baby food, operating in a basement with no anaesthetic, as all the windows above ground level had been shot out. One day our vehicle got shot by snipers, bursting a tyre. If there was one thing Bosnian Serb and Muslim fighters liked less than journalists, it was women journalists. As the great British army helped change our tyre, I was told to stay in the vehicle with my helmet pulled low to my eyes and my flak jacket on. I filed my report for Radio 1 and David filed his for the *Daily Mail* and money poured in for Feed the Children. I returned once more, this time for the *Evening Standard* and recall a woman at a makeshift orphanage quietly explain to me that she was helping there because her two children had been shot in front of her and she didn't want to see any others suffer more than they already had. Her strength was humbling.

When I got home, I was walking to my car after a long shift at the *Daily Express*. A car backfired and I jumped 10 feet in the air. To be a war reporter and remain unaffected by what you see and hear is impossible if you have any heart whatsoever.

***

Back in the *Daily Express* bar some months later, in 1994, conversation turned to Nelson Mandela, who was expected to be elected the first black president of South Africa. This would also be the first time black South Africans would be allowed to vote. Danny McGrory encouraged me to cover the story. I protested that I knew very little about South Africa and he said, 'Well do your homework.' So I did, spending hours in the newspaper library after work and more on the phone and online, securing contacts at all the political parties fighting for election. I won commissions from several titles including the *Telegraph* and the *Sunday Mirror* and headed off for six incredible weeks where I walked at the shoulder of Nelson Mandela almost daily as he addressed stadiums of supporters around the country; interviewed his first wife Evelyn in KwaZulu Natal with my new photographer friend Tom Stoddard taking her photo and his eldest daughter Makaziwe in Johannesburg. I sat in the African National Congress head office and interviewed Mandela's trusted comrades Thabo Mbeke and Walter Sisulu, who would both succeed him as ANC president, about the future South Africa they hoped to see. Danny McGrory showed me how to cover a march of hundreds of Zulus in traditional dress in Johannesburg, in support of their leader Mangosuthu Buthelezi – always at the front, never in the middle or behind – and a riot in Joburg. And I saw history change, as black South Africans of all ages patiently queued to cast their vote for the first time. The vote count took over a week and I spent that time working for the South African *Sunday Times* in Johannesburg, during which time I interviewed Antoinette Sitole, the sister of Hector Pieterson, in Soweto. Pieterson was fatally shot in 1976, during the Soweto Uprising, a protest by black school children, against Afrikaans and English being the only languages to be spoken in schools. And I met up with Michael Buerk at BBC HQ, as we discussed the ANC and National Party and the future of South Africa. All those years ago, I wanted to be having the adventures he was having and now I was.

I returned home to hear that Mandela had been elected and went back to working as a jobbing news reporter, covering further foreign assignments as I uncovered stories, including street children being shot in Rio de Janeiro, Sierra Leone repairing from its civil war and I returned to South Africa at any opportunity, usually to write about conservation and the decline in wild animal populations.

***

I had always put my job first. I'd cancelled social events and dates with boyfriends in favour of my career. A few times I was offered opportunities to move to the news desks and commission others but I loved writing, travelling, new experiences, cultures and thinking on my feet. That changed one day when I met my husband for the first time, at a salsa class at the Rivoli Ballroom in south London that I was dragged along to by my friend Carol. We met the next day and every day for three months, until the house I was renting with four others was put up for sale and I moved into Michael's home. I had always valued my independence and hadn't let any man get this far into my world – until now.

Every year I had covered the prestigious Brit Awards for the *Daily Mail*. It was always a fun, ostentatious event, filled with music's glitterati and a firm date on my calendar. When the call came, I already had a date lined up with Michael. After a few fair-weather relationships, I had finally met a man I didn't want to cancel on and I passed up the job. He made me laugh and danced and didn't try to impress me. Instead, he was quieter than some of the boyfriends I'd had previously but more sincere than all of them put together. Twenty-five years later, we are still having date nights and adventures of our own and have two wonderful teenagers to complete our family. The arrival of my children heralded my decision to no longer cover news stories that would pose a threat to my safety and to remain closer to home. I became a features writer for magazines, which fitted neatly around my family life. Later, I changed careers and moved into the fitness industry, a little later than most and you know the rest.

***

My life hasn't been smooth or easy. But it hasn't been wasted either. Like most of us who have got over half way through our lives, I have hit a lot of junctions, when

I've had to choose between turning left or right, some more painful than others. I've been knocked down and got back up again. I've climbed mountains, literally and figuratively. I've met those who doubted my ability or motives and had to believe in myself and move towards my goals regardless. I've encountered those who abused my trust and friendship but also far more who have had my back and stood at my side. I could have said no to new opportunities, of course, and found excuses to make my life easier. But the memories I hold now because of those decisions are so valuable. I'm really glad I didn't.

It's because I value the good times that I fought so hard to get through cancer when it came calling. I have an annual abdominal ultrasound scan, to be certain of no further tumours and I would be lying if I said it didn't make me anxious each year, but as time passes, I become less worried.

I don't just celebrate each New Year, I celebrate each new day. Who am I? I'm whoever I want to be. The decision is mine and I'll own it.

WHO ARE YOU?

Changing Direction

I'VE described the highs – mostly highs – and lows that have led me to my current life. I'm not defined by my past, but it does influence my decision making and the actions I take to create my present and future. So, who are you and who do you want to be? I think it's important to ask ourselves this question regularly. I apply it twice a year, during annual breaks from routine in the summer and at Christmas. I ask myself whether life is moving in the right direction, if it's moving too fast or too slow. I consider whether there are new goals I want to achieve or long-term goals that keep slipping away from me and why this is happening. When I have answers to these questions, I set about making a new plan for the next six months. This might involve a diary re-set or some research or seeking advice. It might mean a small adjustment or a major shift.

I also ask myself what I want less of in my life. Maybe this is wasted hours scrolling social media or an aspect of work or a hobby that is no longer fulfilling and I then set about pushing these things aside. To make change, we need to assess our fears around the consequences of our actions and come to terms with these before we move on.

The big positive to be gained by letting go of the aspects of our lives that aren't satisfying, is that we create more available time to do the things that are pleasurable and to be with the people who make us smile. Being still and quiet enough to think clearly helps me reach these conclusions and not be muddled about my objectives.

Each Christmas, my husband prints photos of the places we've been and things we have done during the previous 12 months. It's my favourite gift as it's such a lovely reminder. Not every year is easy but we can create light moments on the greyest of days. When I was ill, it was the smallest things that brought joy, the scent of a refreshing face wash, daffodils poking their cheery heads above the ground in spring, a rainbow. These small positive things mattered a great deal and gave me the strength to push on.

***

Change Following Trauma

Of course some changes are not of our own making and we are forced to adapt. When we are going through trauma, it's even more important to activate the pause button, or risk being consumed by a situation that appears beyond our control. 'When we are going through a change of circumstances, we talk about getting back to normal,' says consultant psychiatrist Phil Hopley. 'The idea of getting back to normal is interesting in itself. What do we mean by normal? There isn't always an obvious cut off for what's normal and what's abnormal. We can use the term functioning more helpfully here. Wanting to get back to doing the things that we can do well post-trauma, means re-calibrating fear and anxiety around what has happened and the fear that it will happen again, to manage any lasting impact.'

Gaining perspective when we feel threatened by our situation is vital. Phil Hopley adds: 'The range of responses to trauma is very broad. People respond in different ways, in different scenarios. When attention is being drawn to one particular thing that is upsetting or concerning, it's important to put into context how important that thing is. You may be fearing that you will be defined by your trauma and that this will change the perception others have of you and what you have achieved to date. We call this catastrophising,' he says. 'This is concentrating on possible outcomes without having evidence to support them. It comes back to perception and recognising unhelpful imbalanced thinking. When you are in the eye of the storm, you are emotionally aroused and in a threat state. Your attention is drawn to the threat and it's very hard to draw your attention away from the thing that is causing the distress or disquiet.

'My advice is to break the fixation on the negative thoughts around that situation. It's helpful to distract and engage ourselves in other areas that are interesting or exciting or fun. Pointing people to pastimes, to doing things with their families is a good way of doing that.

'Mindfulness is one of the best ways of helping people develop a strategy to better direct their thoughts. There are some very affordable apps available to help with this, like *Buddhify*, *Calm* and *Headspace*. They take someone who hasn't had any experience of mindfulness through the steps needed to take better controlled direction of their attention and thought patterns.'

***

Will Trauma Change You?

When I received my diagnosis, I worried about how I would be defined by others. I was a mother, a wife and a successful journalist. I was an organiser, a doer and liked to be kept busy. A friend used to say I moved at warp speed, as I fitted lots into my day. I liked being an achiever. I wanted to be accepted for being these things. I didn't want to be 'the woman with cancer.' But trying to change the way others see us isn't possible. We have no control over the thoughts of other people. More importantly, it doesn't matter. It's how we perceive ourselves that wealds us so much more power.

'So much of this is about meaning,' says Phil Hopley. 'Will trauma change us? Yes, of course. It may have profound effects on us. A painful, damaging relationship with someone you had trusted can cause a lack of intimacy with others going forward. It's important to realise that anything in life can change us but we do have choices about our behavioural responses. Does it have to define us? Not necessarily. Some of us will get stuck and have our own narrative that can be a disabler, where we feel victimised and helpless. At that point professional help needs to be sought. Working with a psychiatrist can help us to see that what is happening to us is through our choice and it is leaving us perpetually in a cycle of rumination and revaluation of what we have been through.

'There is no one way of focusing and moving on. It's a different approach for everyone. For some people, going back and reprocessing the trauma with cognitive behavioural therapy (CBT) or eye movement desensitisation and reprocessing (EMDR) can be helpful and powerful. Others are not at a stage where they can do that and they just need the ability to survive day to day to do the basics,' he admits.

'Others make a healthy adaptation of their situation by becoming advocates for change and support for others going through a similar situation, when they find peace with their own personal circumstances.'

***

Blame

Accepting that only we can change our situation is the first step towards creating the life that we want for ourselves. Blaming others for our past and apportioning blame for the situation we find ourselves in now is easy but also futile. It achieves nothing. It's a negative action. As we try to create a new future, blaming others halts our progress and it slams our recovery into reverse, as we succumb to an ever increasing cycle of debilitating anger and frustration. If we take the same energy we are using for blame and anger and apply it positively, in the smallest of ways each day, we start moving away from an unhappy place and closer to creating a life where we have calm and become in control of our destination.

***

One Foot in Front of the Other

Some days, trying to look at our whole situation and wanting to change it can seem overwhelming. On days when it all seems too much, I tell myself that all I'll do is put one foot in front of the other, stopping when I need to, then pick my feet up again when I'm ready and carry on. This has been particularly useful when I've been dealing with wounding bereavements that deliver a big grey cloud, where energy once was. I take off the pressure to achieve and just try to get through the day. Then try again tomorrow. And that's enough.

The next day I repeat the process but try to add one thing that will make me happy – tending my garden, listening to music, watching a distracting comedy or walking my dog. I keep interaction with others to a minimum and keep quiet, giving myself space and time to process my thoughts and gain some clarity and perspective.

The next day I start to process the problem, breaking it into manageable chunks and take one decisive step. It might be a difficult phone conversation or email. When that's done, I look at the next step but there's no rush. When our life has had a grenade thrown into it, there is rarely a quick fix to put the fire out. We can stand by and watch that grenade burn everything we hold dear or we can tackle it, one section at a time. The more steps I take, the more control I gain and the less overwhelmed I feel.

***

Chunking It Down

Taking a challenging situation, whether it is of our own making or not, and chunking it down into manageable bites is vital because it makes what is confronting us less overwhelming. I interviewed endurance athlete Dean Karnazes, an ultra-runner whose achievements include running 350 miles in 80 hours, 44 minutes without sleep and winning the 135-mile Badwater Ultramarathon across Death Valley, as the eastern California desert scorched in a 120 degrees Fahrenheit furnace. The distances and conditions he has endured are beyond the capability of most experienced, capable runners. Completing a marathon is relatively simple. You follow a plan, get the miles in your legs, build up muscle memory and take on the right nutrition and hydration.

Planning an endurance event requires all of those things and huge reserves of mental strength. Dean explained that whatever his race or destination, his plan is underpinned by the same philosophy. As he runs, he doesn't consider the overall distance. Instead, he will run to the next tree, then on to the next lamp post, then to the parked car. During his races, he runs past thousands of trees and lamp posts and cars but only ever focuses on one at a time. It's a really useful mind trick. Dean chunks down his goal distances. He has a saying that I like a great deal, too, 'Run when you can, walk if you have to, crawl if you must but never, ever give up.'

Phil Hopley recalls, 'I worked with a client who set out to run 50 marathons in 50 days. He trained relentlessly. We talked about him keeping focus. He would be on the road and his mind would turn to the ache in his calf. His mind should be anywhere but there because the more attention we give to the ache or any pain or discomfort, the more we fuel it. It's like throwing petrol on a fire which gets the mind into a very unhealthy focus. On day five, he ran into a pot hole at night and tore a quadricep muscle. He had huge amounts of sponsorship and was doing it for charity. His times had been good, at around four and a half hours for each marathon. The next few days took nine hours over the same distance. Using the approach of taking his challenge in bite size chunks, he completed it, still injured. He went on to run his personal best time on his 49th marathon, completing it in just over three hours. When we are challenged, it's vital to have our mind on our side to overcome negative thoughts, to be positive as much as we can and to anticipate where we will face difficulties. It doesn't matter whether it's an athletic challenge or a big new goal we are working towards, or a professional, relationship or family problem. We need to find ways to break it down into manageable, achievable targets. Once we do that, we move against the brain's tendency to see a situation as insurmountable.

'I have worked with some unbelievable athletes over the years, in a far-reaching range of sports, including boxing, tennis, rugby, cricket, football,' he adds. 'The ability of someone to fulfil their potential when they are physically capable, is always down to their mindset. The saying, 'Whether you think you can or you think you can't, you are probably right,' is very true. I have seen athletes pull performances out of the bag that they weren't previously capable of due to their mindset on the day. I worked with a medallist rower, in the run up to the Olympic Games. Even though he was physically in top condition, his attention got diverted and his performance went in the wrong direction. Thoughts are not who we are. They are just pieces of mental activity that happen and we can choose to engage with them or resist them. We need to try to engage with the ones that are constructive and positive and helpful and move away from thoughts which are not.'

***

What Are You Afraid Of?

Change, whether it is of our making or not, can be scary and some of us are more resistant to it than others. Those of us with a negative disposition, whose cup is usually half empty, will question all the things that could go wrong. Those with a generally positive outlook, whose cup is usually half full, will concentrate their thoughts on the benefits of altering their direction and all the things that could go right. It's usual and sensible to measure the possible impact of change. 'A useful starting point would be to acknowledge that most humans are fearful of change,' explains Phil Hopley. 'The human brain prefers predictable outcomes. One of the things that gets in the way of making change is predictability. Human brains like the world to be predictable because the fight or flight response is less likely to be triggered in areas where we know what is happening to us'.

He adds, 'Fear creates a physiological response in our bodies. The stress hormone cortisol leads to adrenalin release which is essential for short-term survival for the muscular skeletal system, the respiratory system, cognitive function, nervous system and visual accuracy. All of these things get dialled up. At the same time, other areas get dialled down – our gastrointestinal system, our reproductive system, our auto immune system – all the areas that are not essential for short-term survival. The stimulation that causes fight or flight means we may feel that sensation of butterflies in our stomach or that our muscles feel tense or we may feel restless.

'However, fighting change is going to be counterproductive. It's going to make the mental effort required for change even harder because by resisting change, we are putting our brains into that fight or flight scenario. That's mentally and physically draining. We need to look at whether our perception of change is accurate. If it isn't, we need to look at what we can do to be more realistic about what is about to happen. For some people that's a one to one discussion. For others it's talking to colleagues or family about how situations like this have been dealt with successfully previously,' he says.

***

Self-Care

Most of us have busy lives and many of us have others who depend on us, one way or another. There are tasks that are expected of us by others. They may be menial and not very rewarding but our lives become more uncomfortable if they aren't completed.

Try this. List three things you do on a daily or weekly basis for other people. My guess is that they come to mind quite quickly. Now, name the one thing you really want to do for yourself. This is personal to you and has nothing to do with what others may want you to do or what they may want to do themselves. It's the thing that makes you smile, the thing that makes your heart beat a little faster when you bring it to mind. Maybe it's the thing you have been dreaming of for years but haven't dared to try it yet. Now list three things that are stopping it happening. These might be not having enough information, or cost, or available time. Next, list three things you can do to make that special thing for you happen. Maybe it's research to find out how, when and where you can do it. If it's cost, start exploring how you can afford to do it, perhaps missing out on your daily cappuccino on the way to work or your weekly takeaway and saving up these pounds or taking on another job or extra hours. If it's available time to make a commitment, take a long hard look at your diary and find the gaps. Add the thing that is special to you to these gaps and ring fence this time. Make it important and don't get distracted or give this time up for others. This is your special thing. Wouldn't it be disappointing if it never happened? Now isolate one of those actions and do it today.

***

Say No

It's usually easier to say yes than to say no. But how many times do we find ourselves doing things we resent because we took the easy option? Saying no, politely but firmly, can take practice if we are a people pleaser and used to saying yes and following the crowd. But when we start saying no, we come to realise that it's empowering. The world keeps turning and those people we said no to don't think any less of us for doing so. Most importantly, it means that by saying no to the things we don't want to do, we are creating time and space to do the things that are important to us and make us happy.

LOSS

THERE is no positive spin to offer here. Just, I hope, a few helpful sources of information to navigate the grieving process. As with all trauma, our circumstances are unique and how we manage them, day to day, week by week, month by month, is governed by our previous experience, if any, of loss. If we were in denial about our grief during a previous bereavement, a new loss can unearth the desolate feelings we experienced last time which can seem overwhelming. Whether it's one trusted friend or professional advice from a grief counsellor, it's important to talk, when we feel ready. If we don't feel able to reach out straight away, it might be that the first anniversary of our loss brings new pain and those wounds can be treated by sharing how we feel with a non judgemental individual, who can work through our feelings with us. There's never a right time to seek help. Only the right time for us.

When my father died, the loss was sudden. As it was suicide and linked to drug addiction, and there wasn't a big mental health conversation in the 70s, his death wasn't spoken about. I struggled through my teenage years until finally visiting his grave alone one day after school and making my peace with his death. Questions about my father were raised by my husband when we met and my children, curious about their grandfather. It was important to reach my peace with his death, before having those conversations and I'm pleased I had. Some of my questions will remain unanswered; and that's ok. My sisters and mother had to go through their own grieving process. My father isn't forgotten and is still discussed occasionally between us, but we have all moved on from those traumatic early years.

Before our children were born, I had a miscarriage early on in pregnancy. We had been trying for a baby for two years and this loss was devastating. I wanted to run away, start a new life and forget about everything. The pain of loss was physical, like I was punched in the stomach daily. With the gentleness and kindness of my grieving husband, we gradually moved forwards, together.

***

I lost three friends in quick succession during the Coronavirus pandemic lockdown. These weren't people on the periphery of my life. These were trusted confidantes from different areas of my life. Between them, we shared 50 years of adventure and excitement and propped each other up in times of distress. These were the kind of friends you could message at 1am and without hesitation, they would hear you out and be at your side and I would do the same for them. Losing the first one was devastating. Losing the second was crueller still. When the third died, I was finding daily life difficult to manage. Funerals were for close family only, to prevent Coronavirus spreading further and there were no wakes. There was no opportunity to celebrate their lives, nor share in grief, which weighed heavy.

I decided that I needed to act in order to move forwards. One sunny day, a month after the third death, as lockdown rules relaxed, I did something I had always wanted to and booked a wing walk. I decided to use it to raise money for a hospice which had helped my friends. I printed off their photos, along with the photo of another dear friend who had died just a few short months before lockdown and slid them inside my shirt on the day. I told them we were going on one last adventure. My family came to the airfield, along with the closest family of those who had died. I felt they were nearby during the 15-minute flight. Soaring through a cloudless blue sky, I smiled more broadly than I had in a long time. Their families admitted it was an emotional day but that it had helped them too. From that day on, the grief caused by losing those four friends became easier to bear and my heart felt lighter.

***

Consultant psychiatrist Phil Hopley comments, 'When someone is grieving, the most important organ in losing another person is the heart. In feeling that loss and grieving, we feel that some part of us has gone with them. The mind responds to this and the emotional cycle begins and takes us through the usual bereavement process of sadness, anger and acceptance. We hope to move through these without too much disruption, although some people will be in denial that the person has gone and will get stuck at various stages along the way. Most people will have a healthy bereavement cycle and begin to accept the loss of that person at between six to 12 months and start to use the memory to trump the feelings of pain and sadness with pleasing reminders of them. It varies so hugely between individuals and between cultures and nations and family groups. The way we celebrate or appreciate life can be hugely comforting and help us move forward.'

***

How You Can Help Yourself

If you are enduring bereavement, don't feel you have to paint on a smile. Also, know that your feelings at the start of each day and throughout each day will vary. Consciously consider each morning how you are feeling. What can you achieve today? Only set yourself tasks that are manageable and that you feel comfortable with. Do you need to cancel appointments? Do you need to get outside of your home and breathe fresh air? Make a plan in accordance with how you are feeling and please yourself. The world will keep turning without you at that meeting and welcome you back when you are ready to take a bigger role. Feel under no pressure whatsoever to please anyone else. Take each new day as it comes.

***

Helping an Adult Cope With Grief

Stay in contact and let them know you are thinking of them. Let them know they are not alone. Let them discuss their feelings. Talking can be one of the most helpful things after someone dies. Don't give opinions or advice about what they should or shouldn't be doing, however well intentioned. Don't tell them you know how they are feeling. Each bereavement is unique. Just listen and be near. You cannot fix their pain but you can make them feel less lonely.

Make a note of important dates that may cause distress, such as birthdays and the anniversary of their loss and let them know you are thinking of them at these times.

Andy Langford, Clinical Director of Cruse Bereavement Care adds: 'Let them grieve at their own pace. Don't rush them. There is no timeline to follow here. Let them talk about how they are feeling and about the person they have lost. Talking can be very helpful, even if you find it difficult to hear because of your own grief and you are unable to make their pain go away.

If you feel they aren't coping, encourage them to seek professional help.

On significant dates, such as birthdays or the anniversary of their death, remind them that you are thinking of them.'

***

Helping a Child Cope With Grief

Children and young people need to be given time and space to grieve. It's important to remember that they grieve in different ways. A child's understanding of death and bereavement will be different at different stages of development and each child will respond in different ways.

Teenagers have developed a deeper understanding of death and the long-term implications of losing someone close and are more keenly aware of the emotional aspects.

Allow them to talk and do not be offended if they are angry or do not want to talk. If a child doesn't want to talk, suggest that they could write a letter or poem or draw about how they are feeling.

Remind them that it is ok to feel sad, angry, scared and to cry. It is also ok to feel happy and enjoy things. It is ok if the loved person who has died is not in their thoughts at all times.

Seek professional help if you need to discuss how best to support a child through grief.

Andy adds: 'Consider whether your child should attend a funeral. It can help a child understand the finality of death, to join family and friends to say goodbye. Explain there are no set feelings they should experience at this time and include them in planning the funeral if they feel they wish to be involved. They may want to write something to be read during the ceremony but it's important that they don't feel under pressure to attend or be involved. Explain that they can change their mind, even at the last minute.'

***

Loss of a Child

Losing a child is not the natural order of things. It is expected that a child will outlive his or her parents and grandparents. When this order is disturbed, the recovery process is complicated by passing time, as we remember each birthday we would have celebrated with them, the adventures they would have lived and maybe their wedding day and their own children. The grieving process is a long, hard road.

Phil Hopley comments, 'Coming to terms with this is very difficult. Part of the challenge is dealing with the understandable questions of why them, why not us, what was it that led to this? It's hard to move on. But looking at the fond memories, the happy photograph, can start to heal the pain. A simple exercise is literally looking back through letters teachers had written at school and family photograph albums as part of a response to that lost life. It can be a very comforting, practical approach that we can take.'

If we have lost a child before pregnancy is complete, the grieving process is equally complex. Globally, one in 10 pregnancies will end in a preterm birth but how we each respond to loss is unique. Losing a new life, through miscarriage or stillbirth, someone you have not had an opportunity to get to know, can be devastating. Tommy's, which supports research into miscarriage and stillbirth, says, 'When a baby dies or is born too soon, it leaves their parents with so many questions and emotions. Sadly, many of these will go unanswered. It's important that both parents have an opportunity to talk through their grief. Our research team found that one in five women experienced long-term symptoms of post-traumatic stress following an early miscarriage or ectopic pregnancy and one in 12 partners did, too. Both parents will be grieving but partners often get overlooked and it's important that they are given an opportunity to express their feelings.'

Meghan, the Duchess of Sussex spoke candidly about the miscarriage of her second child in the *New York Times*, explaining how an ordinary day had so suddenly been filled with sorrow. She had been playing with her young son when, she says, 'I felt a sharp cramp. I dropped to the floor with him in my arms, humming a lullaby to keep us both calm. I knew as I clutched my firstborn child, that I was losing my second. Sitting in a hospital bed, watching my husband's heart break as he tried to hold the shattered pieces of mine, I realised that the only way to begin to heal is to first ask, 'Are you ok?'' Wise words.

***

Loss of a Parent

It is painful to lose a parent who has enjoyed a long and happy life. If they die unexpectedly, at a young age, this adds more complex emotions to the grieving process. The death of a parent changes many aspects of our lives and has an impact on the whole family. As with all loss, there is no right way to grieve, as everyone experiences bereavement differently.

Andy Langford comments, 'As well as shock or numbness, people often feel regret, guilt or anger. We may feel very different from one moment to the next and the feelings can often contradict each other. They may come upon us when least expected, which can be confusing or distressing.

'We can feel lost after the death of a mother or father. Suddenly we may find ourselves feeling like a child again, even though we are adults with jobs, families and lives of our own.

'Losing a parent may mean losing one of the people who thought we were the most special and who loved us unconditionally. Alternatively, if we had a difficult or estranged relationship with a parent, we can feel a grief for what never was, or for a relationship it is now not possible to heal.

'The death of a parent can bring home the inevitability of our own death, and perhaps make it seem nearer than it was before.

'The balance of generations changes when a parent dies. Before, we were someone's child. Now we can find ourselves the older generation and that can be a shock.

'Losing a parent or both parents means we may also have lost a connection to our own childhood. We have lost someone who could talk to us about our early years and share memories in a way no one else can.

'A death in the family can bring people together but it can also unearth old rivalries and create tension between siblings. Some may feel able to support each other and others may feel they can't share their feelings and prefer to be left alone.

'We may have looked after an ill parent for some time and this role has now disappeared. This can come as a release but also lead to a sense of isolation.'

Andy Langford suggests the following steps after the death of a parent:
Talk to someone:-
'Talking can be really helpful, even if it is over the phone or internet or social media. If you have a faith, you may be able to speak to a spiritual leader. Do talk to your GP if your health is suffering.'

Find ways to remember them:-
'Try to find ways you can remember your parent and keep them as part of your life. This might mean keeping a few special possessions, creating a memory box or a special album of photographs or organising a time for the family to come together and remember.'

Plan ahead on anniversaries:-
'Birthdays, anniversaries, Mother's Day and Father's Day can be difficult after a parent dies as can that first Christmas. It can help to think in advance about how to manage these times.'

***

Loss of a Partner

When we lose someone we love, we lose not only someone who was special to us and unique but also a relationship that was cherished. Losing a husband, wife or partner is intensely emotional. Our world changes and accepting this can be incredibly painful. It can mean coming to terms with a change of identity, the loss of future dreams to be shared together, feelings of isolation, financial loss, increased household responsibility and a feeling of vulnerability.

Andy advises, 'After the funeral of a partner, and the weeks of practicalities around their death, it can feel like things start to return to normal for others, but for you nothing will be the same. Friends and family start to check in with you less often and the world keeps turning but you are facing a future without your life partner, an empty space at the dinner table or beside you in bed.

'It's usual to feel mixed feelings, including loneliness, sadness, despair, emptiness, anger or guilt. The person who has died is physically absent but the feelings you have for them continue. In addition, we may be missing the physical closeness and intimacy of our partner. It's not unusual to feel restless, irritable, a lack of motivation and concentration. It's common to experience headaches, weight loss, sleep disturbance or fatigue. If symptoms persist, it's sensible to consult your GP.

'After a year has passed, others may be expecting you to feel more confident but many feel the second year can be just as hard as the first. This doesn't mean that others have forgotten your partner, just that their life has progressed in a way yours cannot. There is no set timeline for grief and the experience is different for everyone. Do what feels right for you, prioritising yourself and those you are responsible for, such as children. Grieving cannot be rushed.

'Sometimes, we can feel a pressure to move on and find a new partner. The decision needs to come from you and what feels right at the time. Some don't feel ready for a new partner for years or never. It's very much an individual decision.'

Andy Langford suggests the following steps after the loss of a partner:
Choose someone you feel comfortable with, a friend, family member or someone from your church if you have a faith. Or seek grief counselling if you prefer to talk to someone unconnected to your partner.

It's important to acknowledge that although your partner may have died, the memory of them does not. It can help to think of ways you can keep your partner as part of your life. Consider creating a memory box of possessions or special photo album or a time for family or friends to come together and remember them.

If you are struggling financially or are overwhelmed by financial matters, contact Citizens Advice, who will help you get organised and claim benefits if you need to.

***

Traumatic Loss

When someone we love dies in a traumatic situation, there are additional problems that add to our grief. The sudden finality of that person's loss, without the opportunity to say goodbye, if we witnessed their sudden death or were absent for it, or if it was caused by others, all complicate the grieving process.

Andy advises, 'Losses for which we are unprepared are difficult to make real, especially if we are unable to say goodbye to that person. If this has happened to us, it can take a long time to accept. Everyone will react in different ways but it may help to visit the place where the person has died, talk with others involved or attend a memorial service. Be prepared to live with the knowledge that what happened may never be explained. Some will be haunted by pictures in their mind of the traumatic event. These may be triggered by reminders, such as loud noises, cries or shouts. Some may resort to shutting themselves away at home to avoid these reminders. At its most severe, this can result in post traumatic stress disorder, which can be disabling and need professional psychological help.

'Grief is the natural response to the loss of a loved one. It is more likely to cause problems if it is bottled up rather than expressed. Some will need to cry or rage and others will talk about what has happened, to try to make sense of a traumatic death.

'Sometimes we feel the need to punish ourselves. We think, 'Why should I be happy?' when that person has died. We may blame ourselves for their death, especially if we were not there when they died. Grief is not a duty to the dead. Those we love would not want us to suffer.

'We may feel angry, particularly if the death has been caused by violence or terrorism or negligence or error. Some will find themselves hitting out at the people they love most. If you have said or done things that have hurt others, don't be too proud to apologise.

'If someone close dies by suicide, the grieving process can be difficult to resolve. We may feel anger towards the person who died for not asking for help or not saying goodbye or leaving us.

'Overwhelming guilt is common following suicide. We may feel guilty for things we did or didn't say or do. Try to remember all the things you did do for the person who has died.

'We may torture ourselves by asking why or what if and if we could have prevented the suicide in some way. It can be difficult to come to terms with missing answers that can only be given by the person who has died.

'Try talking about how you are feeling or writing down your thoughts. Look at pictures and visit meaningful places. Light a candle at a certain time each week as a lasting memorial.'

***

Loss of a Pet

Our pet animals have their place in our homes. They can be a great comfort at times of distress, a reason to remain active when our instinct is to isolate and bring great joy. Losing a pet can be distressing for the whole family and devastating for those who live alone. Diana James, manager for Blue Cross for Pets comments, 'Feelings of despair, loneliness and depression can be overwhelming, following the loss of a pet. When the love and friendship of a pet are gone, life may suddenly seem very empty. There may also be a sense of guilt when a decision has been made to euthanise. These feelings are testament to the special bond between people and their pets.

'We often hear that friends and colleagues don't understand the upset that losing a pet can bring. Grieving for a pet can be a very lonely experience. It can help to share our feelings with someone who knows from personal experience how distressing the loss of a pet can be and who will listen with compassion and without judgement.'

***

The human experience of happiness, sadness, love, loss, success, failure, is shared by us all, though our lives may take many different paths. 'I Did It My Way' is the advice of some trusted friends, who generously talked to me about some of their toughest times and, with hindsight, the advice they would have given themselves during that trauma.

I Did It My Way

'My wife Christine and I were married for over 30 years when she died of lung cancer. Initially, it was caught early and the tumours removed. Unfortunately, she struggled to give up smoking, despite trying hypnosis and all sorts of therapies and the cancer returned. I was so angry, as I knew that if she couldn't give up smoking, it was a waiting game before she would be gone. I stayed angry until I started putting together the order of service for her funeral. I started to look back at the amazing life we'd had together and 30 years of memories and that was a turning point for me. I decided that I would remember all the good times with Christine, the woman I fell in love with, and push the last two years of our lives together to the back of my mind. That's what I've done ever since.' –

Simon Porter

'The worst time for me was when my dad died after a long illness. I spent seven years preparing for it. When it came, the grief was tough but I realised that's life and the world keeps turning. When your loved ones pass, they want you to live your life and would hate you to be unhappy. Pick yourself up, dust yourself off and make them proud. Embrace the storm and push on.' –

Chris H

Useful Contacts:

Cruse Bereavement Care helpline
0808 808 1677

Citizens Advice national phone line
0800 144 8848

Child Bereavement UK helpline
080002 888 40

Young Minds helpline
0808 802 5544

Survivors of Bereavement by Suicide helpline
0300 111 5065

Samaritans helpline
116 123

Tommy's
0207 398 3400

Blue Cross Pet Bereavement Support Service helpline **0800 096 6606**

MANAGING PHYSICAL CHANGE

WHEN we are unhappy with our appearance and choose to make changes to our body, for improved physical or mental health, we can research the steps and commitment that are required, assess the risk and make an informed choice about how we take this forwards.

A trauma that leads to physical change that is not of our choosing, through illness or injury, is often followed by a mental health battle before we reach an acceptance stage and make peace with our altered situation. Asking for help here is the first step to moving forwards but that in itself takes courage. It can be hard enough to get used to the changes to your physical appearance and ongoing medical checks and care. You may have to manage the reactions of members of your family; older and younger individuals may react differently. It may alter the outlook of friends or limit the social life and activities you had previously enjoyed. You may feel angry or depressed and endure a grieving period for the body you previously knew. Your altered body may limit physical activities that you had enjoyed before your body changed and you may have to make alterations to your living arrangements and change the way you work. Feeling less independent can be suffocating but with the help of those close to you and agencies who can offer practical and emotional help and advice, it's possible to move on to the next phase of your life, with purpose and goals.

Consultant psychiatrist Phil Hopley adds, 'It's important to accept that physical change is not always negative. People make physical change just through ageing, by altering body shape and becoming healthier. Some will take the changes they make to their bodies to an extreme, maybe as they get a little too fond of looking muscle bound or by changing the appearance of their face with surgery on a regular basis and those people may benefit from some counselling to make sure there are no underlying mental health issues.

'Those who encounter a physical change due to acute trauma, perhaps a vehicle accident, or fire or military service, are faced with sudden change. The fact that it is a sudden loss is going to compound the experience. The context will affect how we respond to trauma. Internal resources that people have used to cope with other difficulties over the years may be a clue to how they will cope here. Family, friends, peer, medical and social support are all important. For someone with a life changing injury, this is vital.'

He adds, 'Some, like former rugby player Ed Jackson, took on endurance events to help himself and others, following paralysis caused by a diving accident. Others are overwhelmed by what has happened to them. It comes back to fight or flight again. Some will not cope and if they don't address their emotions it can be very destructive.'

I look at a few physical conditions here. There are many more of course but whatever the situation, there are some recurring pieces of advice. Ask for help. Talk about how you are feeling. Get practical assistance. Keep your body strong. And never, ever, give up.

***

Amputees

Help For Heroes, who help rehabilitate wounded servicemen and women from the British Armed Forces, say it can take injured veterans three years and nine months to seek help for psychological wounds. Former Royal Marine Commando and father of three Mark Ormrod, MBE, became Britain's first triple amputee to survive conflict, when he stepped on an unexploded device in Iraq in 2007. Prince Harry called him 'Britain's answer to Superman,' after he successfully competed at the Invictus Games but he is the first to admit that creating a new life following active service, meant a long personal journey, as he struggled with his mental health as much as his physical recovery. Mark says, 'The next time you see a baby trying to teach itself how to walk, watch what it does. It fails constantly, but what's beautiful is that a baby doesn't understand the concept of failure so it figures out the last approach didn't work, tries again with a different approach and probably fails again. But it keeps trying. A baby will repeat this formula with no loss of enthusiasm until it eventually works out how to walk and that's when life for that baby reaches a whole new level. It's only when we get older and conditioned by the world around us that we start to think that failure is fatal and we forget that it's a natural part of the process on the path to moving forwards. Embrace the failures. Learn from them. Try not to repeat them and then your life will move to a new level. I keep working on me. The gym is my place, people are going to stare but I don't care. It's my time. It's where I de-stress, empty my mind and refill my energy. It's where I take care of myself physically and mentally. It's how I keep my focus. Exercise makes you harder to kill. It makes me ache less and allows me to think clearly. There are times in life when it's ok to be selfish because it positively impacts all other areas of your life and training does that for me.'

***

Stroke

Over 100,000 of us will have a stroke in the UK each year. That's one in five women and one in six men. We will each have a unique reaction and our own circumstances to manage afterwards. Juliet Bouverie of The Stroke Association explains, 'Some of the most common side effects of a stroke are muscle weakness, paralysis and stiffness in the body. We may struggle with everyday activities and find it harder to move some parts of the body. However, most people will make significant improvements in the first few months. At the Stroke Association, we encourage movement as part of the recovery process from a stroke, to benefit both physical and mental health. Starting to move can be a massive boost to recovery and increased energy. Confidence and well-being all benefit.'

She adds, 'A stroke can affect emotional well-being and lead to a loss of confidence. Many people experience low mood and anxiety after a stroke. Being active can reduce feelings of stress and anxiety and improve low mood. Even if you feel low, it's worth trying some activity, to see what difference it can make. If you are worried about exercising alone, go with a friend. The kind of exercise you can do will depend on your ability and interests. Some may worry that being active will cause another stroke but the opposite is true. Being active is a great way of avoiding another stroke.'

Chris Noble was a keen runner when he had a stroke. 'It was such a shock. I thought of myself as fit and active. But I was also working far too hard and my stroke was caused by stress. My doctor signed me off work for three and a half months so that I could put some distance between myself and the situation that caused the stroke. I became depressed. Some muscles in my face dropped and there was some muscle paralysis and problems with my speech. Gradually these all improved and my confidence returned as I took my dog on daily walks. I reorganised my work, which removed the stress I had been experiencing. Now I love cycling through the countryside. I find that being in nature really helps me.'

***

Brain Injury

Brain injury can severely disrupt cognitive function, sequential movement, create mood swings and affect independence. Recovery takes time and there may be· lasting side effects. Double Olympic gold medallist rower James Cracknell suffered a life threatening brain injury, following a collision with a lorry, while cycling across America. He had to learn to walk, talk and eat. Since then, he has run the London Marathon in two hours and 50 minutes and completed the Yukon Arctic Ultra, also known as The Coldest Race On Earth, in the Canadian Yukon.

As soon as he was able to, James used exercise to help motivate himself back to physical fitness. 'Physical activity and sport were important, as they were things I could control,' he says. 'I kept a diary and monitored my progress. The confidence and self belief you gain when you can objectively see improvements that are of your own doing is enormous and it helps you conquer issues in other areas of your life. I believe in being physically active. It's not just about competitive sport, but about people making the most of their lives.'

***

Dementia

For all life changing conditions, the impact is felt keenly by those close to the person who has encountered change. Research by the Alzheimer's Society shows that around 850,000 people in the UK live with dementia. Each situation is different, just as each person's reaction is unique. The effects on physical and mental health here are unpredictable and distressing. 'The difficulty here is it's not linear. It's hard to predict,' says Phil Hopley. 'What we do know with age related dementia disorders, is that we get short-term memory loss. Long-term memory is largely intact until the very late stages of dementia and carers can use this is a means of communication. Carers need to inform themselves with help from the dementia agencies available to them, as different types of this illness will progress in different ways. Alzheimer's is a relatively quick progression but insidious. In other cases, it's a steady decline, where a vascular event exacerbates the effects of dementia. One of the key things to understand is that it's a terminal illness that we sadly do not recover from.'

***

Hair Loss

Hair loss can be caused by many different triggers and the effects on mental health can be difficult to navigate. Others might comment, in a way that they wouldn't with a different physical change, making the person more self conscious. Trichologist Anabel Kingsley, of Philip Kingsley, says, 'It can be absolutely devastating to a woman who loves her hair. I'll often see tears in the consulting room. They feel they have lost a sense of their own identity. They will say, 'I was known for my hair, my hair was my thing.' When they are losing their hair, women no longer feel like themselves anymore, which can be incredibly depressing. Clients will often avoid social engagements, cancel plans, dread the school run, although no one is looking at your hair with the same degree of vision as you are.' Anabel, whose clients include members of the British royal family and celebrities including Georgia May Jagger, Cate Blanchett, Gwyneth Paltrow and Sigourney Weaver, adds, 'Stress management is very important with any hair loss. We have had a few cases in the clinic where the women have felt suicidal and encouraged them to seek psychiatric help.

'It's not exclusive to women. It is very emotional for men as well. We had a client who felt physical pain when he had his hair cut and have younger men in tears when they lose their hair. There are some treatment options available but we can never guarantee to return hair to its previous state and each client has to find their own management of this change in their appearance.'

There are many types of hair loss, as Anabel explains:

Alopecia Areata

'This is an auto immune condition, where the immune system attacks the hair follicles. Not a great deal is understood about it, although over 90 per cent of cases are triggered by a stressful event. If a member of your family had it, you are much more likely to experience it as well. You are also susceptible if you have another auto immune condition. It affects all age groups but is most common before age 50. I had it after my father, Philip Kingsley, passed away, because of the shock. He was in his mid-80s but very healthy and active and alert and working. He had a stroke so it was very sudden, with no warning. I was expecting some kind of hair loss. It can be associated with bereavement, particularly if you stop looking after yourself. I didn't look after myself at this point and shed some hair. My step sister had it when she was younger. I also have ulcerative colitis, an auto immune condition, so the hair loss with bereavement and shock was not surprising.

'We have a huge number of clients with this condition. It happens with children, too. If you have this prognosis when you are a child, you are more likely to lose more of your hair. When you are older, it may come and go but it is less likely to progress so that you also lose all of your hair.

'It is difficult to fix because it is linked to our immune system. We try various options at the clinic but there is no guarantee of success. It might grow back or it might fall out when treatment stops. UVR therapy of ultra violet light is used to irritate the area, tricking the immune system into recognising those hair follicles as being part of you again. We create a small burn and as cells gather to repair that area, we hope that the immune system then goes back to normal which it often does. We also use a strongly stimulating scalp tonic and cream. Another treatment is systemic or intralesional steroids to lower the immune system but there are more side effects with this and this is not a long-term solution. Vitamin D deficiency has been associated with areata, so we would look into that, also.'

Areata Totalis

'It's much less likely that the hair will come back with totalis. Also there are fewer options available to you. There are immune system suppressant treatments and anti-inflammatory medication that you can take but often the side effects are so severe that they outweigh the benefit of hair regrowth'.

Areata Universalis

'This has a similar prognosis to totalis. You can take medications that your doctor can prescribe. However, the side effects to your general health can be quite severe.'

Male Pattern Baldness

'This makes a pattern on the scalp and is also known as androgenic alopecia. In men, it usually manifests on the temples and crown and can lead to a complete balding of the top of the head, with a horseshoe of hair left underneath. Androgens are male hormones. It occurs when hair follicles on the scalp in genetically pre-disposed areas are sensitive to normal levels of testosterone.

'When the sensitivity is present, hair follicles miniaturise. When the hair follicle is smaller, it produces finer hairs that won't grow as long. The hair will progressively get finer and shorter and the hair follicle may eventually stop producing hair altogether. Once a man is bald, we will tell him that there is not much we can do. Once the hair has gone past a certain point, it's gone and this can be linked to his genetics. It's good to seek help as soon as you notice it. The sooner you treat it, the better the results, as their hair follicle hasn't fully miniaturised.

'If there is still growth, you have two options. Propecia (Finasteride), a 5-alpha reductase inhibitor medication can help stop testosterone from impacting the hair follicles. However, it doesn't work for everyone and can cause side effects, though rarely, such as erectile dysfunction and a lower sperm count, so it's not suitable if you are trying to start a family. There is also topical minoxidil, which can prolong the growth phase of the hair follicle. We prescribe a lotion that contains minoxidil and anti androgens. Often the best results are obtained from using oral Propecia and topical minoxidil together'.

Female Pattern Hair Loss

'This is very similar to male pattern hair loss. Women have lower levels of testosterone naturally. Women hardly ever go completely bald with this. The treatment is the same, except that women do not take Propecia, as it can cause birth defects and there are other really unpleasant side effects for women.

'However, women can take advantage of certain oral contraceptive pills containing anti-androgens, like oestradio, which a man wouldn't be able to take. Oestrogen will help suppress testosterone though we don't want to take too much oestrogen because of the link to breast cancer. If we have a young woman with female pattern hair loss, and she is taking birth control which is anti-androgenic, it can form an integral part of their treatment plan, along with minoxidil and anti-androgens, applied topically to the scalp. Conditions which impact female hormones, such as polycystic ovarian syndrome, which cause the body to produce more testosterone, if you have sensitivity to testosterone, can make it worse. However, anti-androgenic medications can help.'

Hair Loss in Pregnancy

'This is caused by the imbalance of hormones and so many women experience this. Oestrogen is a hair friendly hormone which helps with hair production.

'When oestrogen levels rise in pregnancy, hair is retained in the growing phase. At the end of a pregnancy, many women find their hair is much thicker than it used to be.

'When the hormone levels change, you can experience hair loss. However, some women experience problems with their hair during pregnancy. Women come off the birth control pill to become pregnant. When you become pregnant, this can cause hair shedding in the first trimester. Your hair is heavily relying on diet, so if you suffer severe morning sickness, this can cause hair shedding. Your hair is the last part of you to receive any nutrients you intake and it's the first part of you to have nutrients withheld from, because your body sees your hair as non essential. In the second trimester it can be the same. The third trimester is usually a good time for women's hair but if you have morning sickness into your second trimester or medical conditions as preeclampsia or diabetes or an iron deficiency, this can impact your hair. Many women, approximately 50%, will experience excessive hair shedding six to 12 weeks after giving birth or stopping breastfeeding but re-growth almost always follows. Post partum hair loss occurs because oestrogen levels have declined and all the extra hairs maintained in the growth phase then shed. If you had a traumatic birth and lost a lot of blood, iron deficiency can cause hair loss. If you are not eating well this will also cause hair loss.'

Surgical Change

Consultant plastic, reconstructive and aesthetic surgeon Simon Mackey explains considerations patients should explore before opting for surgery.

'Living with physical change definitely affects confidence. Patients talk of the constant reminder when they take a shower, how their clothes may pull to one side, how self-conscious they are when they take their children swimming and the list goes on. These usual activities suddenly become a major issue. If you lose a limb, have visible scarring from burns or cancer or any other sudden physical change, it's a major reminder of an unpleasant period in one's life. If you are able to restore appearance, you improve daily function.

'When a patient is considering plastic surgery of any kind, their surgeon will often refer them to the hospital psychology unit, who use counselling and CBT (cognitive behavioural therapy) to explore why a patient wants surgery. If they request cosmetic procedures, such as liposuction or breast implants, I always ask if this is for themselves or whether they are being pressured by someone else in their life. The psychology team will explore motives and any previous experiences that may have prompted a desire for surgery.

'It's important that anyone considering plastic surgery has a realistic expectation of how far we can get with their appearance. And it's just as vital that the package of care everyone gets should be tailored to them. Every patient's start point is different and everyone's goal is different.

'The oldest breast reconstruction patient I had was 78. She'd had a mastectomy 30 years earlier, when reconstruction wasn't available and she was told to get on with her life. She decided to change that and was much happier after surgery. Timing is very individual.

'Any anaesthetic surgery has a life threatening risk associated with it. Every surgery has risks associated with it and patients need to be aware of any potential complications.

'It helps if patients can put themselves in a strong position for good recovery. Obesity creates a much greater risk of anaesthetic complications, wound healing problems and other associated issues, so it's important for a patient to get their weight into a healthy range. They can do this by eating a diet rich in good lean protein and a healthy balance of macro and micro nutrients. The more colourful a plate of food is, the better. Smoking is horrendous for anaesthetic risk and wound healing. It's very important to get off nicotine six weeks before surgery and to stay off it until a patient is healed. Not smoking and being a healthy weight is essential for any procedure. The bigger the procedure, the more important it is. The fitter a patient is going into surgery, the quicker they will recover afterwards.'

I Did It My Way

'It's funny, isn't it, how some people shy away from their differences whilst others embrace them. I know it isn't easy. It took me a good few years to accept going from being 6'2" tall, weighing close to 16 stone and having unblemished skin with only one small scar to being a 3'5" tall triple amputee, just over 9 stone and covered in scars. But once I turned that corner I decided that I was going to own it, not only because I wanted to live my life and feel free but because I wanted to encourage others to do the same.

Forget going to the grave in a perfectly preserved body with zero imperfections. Scars tell stories and show that you're a survivor. They show you've been through things and I'm a big fan of showing them off instead of hiding them away.

I haven't used a wheelchair since 2009. Every day I get up at 5.30am, put my prosthetic legs on and provide for my family. My overarching goal is still the same as it's always been - to be the best version of myself.

Embrace your differences, show off your scars, be proud of who you are and what you've overcome. Embrace your uniqueness and walk proudly.' –
Mark Ormrod OBE, former Royal Marines Commando

Useful Contacts:

Philip Kingsley
0207 629 4004

Help For Heroes
0300 303 9888

Stroke Association
0303 3033 100

Headway
0808 800 2244

Alzheimer's Society
0333 150 3456

Samaritans
116 123

YOUTH TRAUMA

A S adults, we have a degree of experience behind us to draw on. When life gets tough, we can consider the scenarios that have gone before and make a measured decision about our next move with the benefit of these.

With fewer years behind them, young people haven't amassed the same amount of emotional intelligence and working through trauma can be overwhelming. The outcome of childhood trauma can influence our adult fight or flight instincts.

Consultant psychiatrist Phil Hopley says, 'It's inevitable that we are going to have some sensitisation based on any early life difficulties that we encounter. We might talk about seeing something which takes us straight back to a much earlier stage of life. An awareness of that is useful. Fight or flight will kick in and the temptation is to run scared.

'It's often easier to see others struggling and pay attention to that rather than dealing with our own issues. Using a check, challenge and change method can help here.

Check
'Ask yourself if that was an adaptive or helpful thought.

Challenge
'If you were a friend or colleague, what would you advise them? This often seems obvious because we tend to be more shy about judging ourselves.

Change
'Change is the approach we make as a result of check and challenge.'

***

In my Fitter Stronger Recharge youth motivation programme, I work with young people of all ages. In each case, they have lost confidence and need to be heard. How we proceed depends on the issues that young person faces. Just as each circumstance is unique, so is each individual's reaction and defence mechanism. However, there are tools that we can use to help young people navigate tough times.

Trust
The young person may feel unable to trust anyone. Accept that if you wish to establish trust, it will take time and patience.

Confidence
If the young person is lacking in confidence, find creative ways to help them see the positives in their life and the positive effect they can have on others. This is a gradual process and small steps are vital here.

Throw a Rope
Remember that you can throw a rope to the person in need but it is up to them to catch it and no amount of you wanting them to can change this. Keep 'throwing the rope' and offering to be a listening ear. Don't give up. After continual refusal, they may surprise you one day and accept your help.

Keep Your Promise

If a young person is feeling compromised and you offer to help, make sure you keep your promise, or you risk losing their trust. If you arrange to talk or meet, do everything you can to avoid cancelling this arrangement.

***

St John Greene is Senior Mentor for youth mentoring group Youth 8, who work with young people aged four to 25 and an emergency medical technician. He explains the signs to look for that may be masking a mental health issue in a young person and some strategies to help them move forwards.

Bereavement

Typical Behaviour

'The young person may internalise their feelings and become depressed. They may worry about their own mortality or that of members of their family or others close to them. They may get angry, which can lead to them getting into trouble, as they can't adequately express themselves and feel unable to control their feelings.

Coping Mechanisms

'Openly talk about the bereavement and listen to their thoughts. Calmly explain that the person who has died would not want them dwelling on the past. Explore the things the young person wants to achieve in their own life. Focus them on working towards these, to make the person who has died proud.

***

Physical and Mental Cruelty From an Adult

Typical Behaviour

'Whether it is sexual or physical assault of a different kind, they will often shy away from any form of touch. If they have been verbally bullied, the young person will often shout back with offensive language when they have an opportunity. Sometimes the sharp language they use is out of context.

Coping Mechanisms

'Talking therapies such as counselling may need to be explored here, to help the young person work through their experience, before they can move forwards. Avoid any kind of physical contact. Keep talking to them to build trust. Engage them in activities you can do together, ideally something outside their comfort zone. The more you share, the more trust builds and they will be more willing to talk about what worries them and work through their thoughts. In doing so, you will create good memories, which will mean they won't be totally focussed on their bad memories. Let them come to you to talk, on their own terms, when they are ready. If they raise their voice, remain calm and ask them how they can express themselves in a different way.

***

Witness to Violent Harm of Someone Else

Typical Behaviour

'Witnessing violence may make the young person perceive that this is normal adult behaviour. They may reflect the same violent behaviour when someone doesn't agree with them. This may be unlike their usual character.

Coping Mechanisms

'If they are showing signs of anger, either because they think this is normal behaviour or because they are angry at what they have witnessed, creative management is required here. Try do a physical activity with them which makes them tired and calm. Consider introducing them to a punch bag and gloves and encourage them to hit with these. Get them to throw a stone as hard as possible into the middle of the sea and do this over and over until they have had enough. These things help focus their anger in a safe environment. Deflecting their anger to diffuse the situation is a useful method here. If they are lashing out, telling them to calm down is not enough. Instead, remain calm and don't show that their angry behaviour is affecting you.

***

Living In a Toxic Situation

Typical Behaviour

'A range of behaviour could be displayed here, from withdrawal to anxiety or anger, depending on the atmosphere the young person is exposed to.

Coping Mechanisms

'If at all possible, spend time with them face to face, in a new environment, rather than virtually. You are removing them from the situation. Letting them talk in a new situation helps them get perspective. Introduce them to youth clubs, sports clubs, dance clubs. Having somewhere safe to spend their down time can be really useful here.

***

Anxiety

'Social cues here will include tics, where the young person is biting their nails, scratching themselves or causing themselves harm in other ways. They might display anti-social behaviour or they may withdraw from a social situation and sit very quietly, away from everyone else, for fear of causing themselves further anxiety.

Coping Mechanisms

'Give them smart objectives. Set them a task and break it into small, simple steps. Find something they can achieve in. It doesn't matter how small it may seem. Each time they achieve a new stage of development, it will give them confidence and help build their resilience. This should be done very carefully, very gradually. Taking small steps here is very important. Also, if you promise to do something with an anxious young person, make sure you carry it out. Structure and framework help here. Disappointment will cause that young person further anxiety and weaken their confidence.

***

Bullying

Typical Behaviour

'This is very different for boys and girls. With boys, it tends to be dealt with physically, in a fight. Girls tend to use psychological warfare and the bullying can be drawn out over a much longer period. With both sexes and non gender specific young people, cyber bullying is also commonplace, which means it doesn't end when the bully and the bullied are no longer face to face. A bullied young person will often withdraw in personality or they may start bullying others.

Coping Mechanisms

'A bullied young person will gain confidence if they have a trusted adult who can support and mentor them. The young person may have been brought up to be sensitive. Bullies tend to pick on the vulnerable. By being a positive role model, you can show them how to not appear vulnerable, by changing their body language. The bullied person will appear more confident if they stand up straight and don't slouch. The better they hold themselves, the stronger they appear. Also, if they are meeting regularly, for instance in school or college, they can position themselves so that they don't have eye contact with the bullies.

'It's often the case that the bullies have been bullied in the past. It may be that this is happening at home and they have become bullies themselves through this learned behaviour. There is usually an underlying reason for bullying. If you are helping a bully, if possible, try to take them out of their comfort zone and into an activity where teamwork is required. If they are working with others they don't know well, it will increase their own self confidence and respect for others.

***

Gang Membership

Typical Behaviour

'It may be that the young person has been picked up from outside of school to be drug carriers or to do porn films or be involved in prostitution. They may be displaying inappropriate behaviour for their age. They may have non-attendance or sporadic attendance at school or college. They may have discovered that they are out of their depth with the gang they are now part of, unhappy and trying to extricate themselves but feel overwhelmed and powerless to do so.

Coping Mechanisms

'If possible, try to get them away from their environment for a few days and separated from their contacts. During that time, ensure their contacts are unable to access them and as they are not of use, they often lose interest in the young person.

'If you are not able to do this, they need a trusted adult to direct them to a safe club, such as a youth club or boxing club but they have to want to go. That trusted adult must know about gang culture or be able to find out significant information from the local police violence reduction unit or similar, in order to be able to mentor them. The aim here is giving the young person enough courage to say no to the gangs. That means building up their self-esteem and resilience. Let them understand that their behaviour is inappropriate, that they are being taken advantage of and that they don't need to be taking a destructive route with their life'.

***

The following are common strategies employed by young people to deflect their mental health struggles. St John Greene explains some ways to identify them and methods to help them change their behaviour.

Obsessive Compulsive Disorder (OCD)

Typical Behaviour

'The young person may be unusually tired. They will often fixate on one activity and repeat it an excessive amount of times throughout the day. There are many possible variants here. These might include cleaning their home or hand washing or showering or repeating a series of tasks several times before leaving the house.

Management

'Use a timer to gradually reduce the time that the young person is doing these activities. Between you, agree an amount of time that they will reduce the activity for one week. The following week reduce the time again, until it becomes less of a focal point for their day and carried out for a sensible duration. Look at how they are filling the rest of their day. Ensure they have something to look forward to each day and discuss anything that they feel overwhelmed by.

Withdrawal

Typical Behaviour

'Look for signs of change in behaviour or routine. The young person may be less willing to socialise and seek excuses to avoid school or college or mix with family or friends. They may lose their appetite.

Management

'Get them to walk and talk if possible. When you do this, you both face forwards as you walk, so the young person knows that you will not be looking at their facial expressions or judging their body language and they won't see yours. You stop when they stop. Like all interventions, they have to want to do this. It has to be on their terms but encouragement is important. If they are willing to engage, there should be no pressure for them to talk. As you talk, encourage them to try one new activity and remind them of the benefit of this. It might be that it's learning a new skill they can share with others or may be something they can add to their CV to assist with college or job interviews.

***

Violence and aggression

Typical Behaviour

'The young person's behaviour may be sporadic or sustained. They may be physically violent or verbally aggressive, towards people they are close to as well as others that they are angry with or scared of.

Management

'If possible, remove the young person from their usual situation. Talking to them in a new environment will help them gain perspective. Explain the consequences of continuing their actions, both for their own safety and for those around them. Depending on the level of aggression, professional help may be needed here to discover the underlying reasons for their behaviour, in order to help them move forwards.

***

Self-Harm

Typical Behaviour

'Signals to look for here include personality withdrawal and anger. The young person is likely to be covering their limbs with long sleeves and trousers, to disguise the scarring caused by their self-harm activities.

Management

'If the young person is cutting themselves, it can feel like a release to them from their anxiety and an adrenaline rush. The act of cutting is employed as a diversion from other pain. Try to give them another outlet for adrenaline, which will scare them but in a good way. Create a positive high by introducing them to challenging activities such as high rope walk centres, abseiling, water skiing, trapeze, rock climbing, which are all done in a safe environment. Talk to them yourself or introduce them to a talking therapist or counsellor who will help them identify the triggers for their behaviour and the underlying cause.

***

Expression of Dark Thoughts

Typical Behaviour

'A young person may describe a willingness to harm themselves or others, a lack of interest in their daily routine or bleak outlook for their future.

Management

'Talking therapies may be needed to discover the root cause of the young person's feelings. Also try showing them ways that they can support themselves and achieve and in doing so, increase their self-esteem. This may mean teaching them how to cook a simple meal that they can survive on. By giving them new skills, you are also giving them control that they haven't felt they previously had. Talk to them about their self-image and counter this with well-being skills. By doing some exercise and managing their nutrition, they gain further control and have a coping mechanism for their feelings and a way to induce calm, clear thought processes. If they are inclined, find ways that they can help others. Being useful to another person will further increase their self-worth.

***

Panic Attacks

Typical Behaviour

'These are typified by anxiety causing the young person to struggle to breathe normally.

Management

'If possible, remove the young person from what is causing the issue. Encourage them to focus on their breathing, taking a breath in through the nose and a longer breath out through the mouth, until their breathing regulates. It may help them to close their eyes or fix their vision on one point. Their anxiety may cause them to shout. Many young people who have panic attacks don't understand their triggers and need to discover these in order to desensitise to whatever is causing the issue.

***

Depression

Typical Behaviour

'Depression can take many forms. Look for lethargy, a loss in appetite, a lack of interest in their daily routine, hygiene or the world around them and a withdrawal from their social life and those they care for.

Management

'Talking therapy or counselling may be required here to discover the underlying cause and help the young person move forwards. If they are willing, encourage them away from their usual routine and into any activity that will improve their self-esteem. This may mean volunteering to help others in any small way that they find acceptable. As they realise they have a useful role to play, their resilience should gradually increase.

Substance Abuse

Typical Behaviour

'Signals here include frequent mood change, poor hygiene and self-awareness, a lack of routine, absence from school or college, secrecy and a change in their circle of friends.

Management

'It is very difficult to get young people off alcohol and recreational drugs unless they want to. Education is the way forward here. Explain the effect of the amount they are taking on their body and the risks to their health. Try deploying a strategy of limiting the amount, agreed between you, when the young person perceives that they need it and reduce it gradually. Ask why they perceive taking these substances is important. Explain addiction and how a small habit can quickly escalate and is then much more difficult to withdraw from. If possible, remove them from their situation so that they cannot access these substances. In addition to this support, seek professional addiction help.

***

Poor Body Image

Typical Behaviour

'Body image is massive with young people, both among their peers and on social media. Those with poor body image or body dysmorphic disorder will focus on their weaknesses. They may appear withdrawn and are likely to wear loose clothing, to avoid showing their body shape.

Management

'Discover how the young person perceives themselves, through gentle conversation, using the walk and talk method, if the young person finds this acceptable. Help them improve their self-esteem by asking them to focus on something that they would like to achieve and take small steps towards this. Talk to them about their well-being. Explain how exercise and good nutrition will give them some control over their body and help them to rest, think clearly and make decisions. Establish the underlying reasons here and suggest counselling for the young person if they wish to engage in this.

***

Low Self-Esteem

Typical Behaviour

'The young person is likely to be focusing on negatives and ignoring any positives in their life. They may seem tired and lethargic and lacking in motivation or interest in themselves or those close to them. They may talk of feeling worthless.

Management

'When a young person presents with low self-esteem, it's important to focus on the positives in their life and what they are able to achieve for themselves. Then show them ways to break this goal down into manageable stages. I explain to the young person who wants to be a car mechanic, working with car engines, that they will be paid more to work with a similar engine on a boat and more still if they work on aeroplane engines. By using their same skills in a different way, they could change how high they aim and how varied their life can be. Low self-worth is a learned behaviour, so try to establish why they feel the way they do. If they are comparing themselves to others, discourage this and focus on their own attributes.'

***

Sleep

Where possible, encourage good sleep protocols. A minimum of eight to nine hours of good sleep is recommended for teenagers. Try to encourage the following to ensure that a young person is getting enough sleep, allowing them to make clear decisions about their well-being:

Limit Screen Time

Agree a time when the young person will turn off their devices. Encourage teenagers to charge their mobile phones, tablets and other blue screen devices in another room or as far away from their bed as possible, so that they are not tempted to reach for them at night. Encourage a teenager to have at least 30 minutes of screen-free time before going to sleep.

Exercise

Encourage a teenager to exercise every day for at least 20 minutes and long enough to get their heart rate up. This will produce dopamine, which will help them sleep later in the day.

Smart Nutrition

Suggest that a teenager drinks less caffeine, found in energy drinks, cola, tea and coffee. These should be avoided altogether after 2pm. Too much caffeine can stop them falling asleep and reduce the amount of deep sleep they have, rendering them tired and irritable the following day. Let teenagers know that eating too much or too little at one time can lead to poor sleep and a lack of energy during the day. Encourage breakfast, lunch and dinner, with small, healthy snacks between these meals.

Keep the Conversation Going

Talk to a teenager about anything they are worried about and keep the conversation going, even if they are quiet and disinterested. By helping to put these worries into perspective, a teenager is likely to sleep better and increase their self-esteem. If they become worried during the day, when you are apart, encourage them to write down their thoughts to discuss with you later and check in with them about these daily.

***

I Did It My Way

'After my dad died, my mum re-married. Life at home with our stepfather became hell on earth. My siblings and I were starved and deprived of clothing and heating. My brother emigrated to Australia, my sister fell pregnant and I joined the army weighing seven stone, so that we could get ourselves new lives. When I left the army, I couldn't get a job and was homeless. I was a young man and I wanted to make my dad proud but couldn't see how. On a freezing cold evening I thought about ending my life. Instead, as a last resort, I called a friend of a friend and asked for help and he invited me to stay with his family. I was then able to get a job as a milkman and turn my life around, eventually running my own business.

When you are at your lowest, it's so important to reach out. I try to help people where I can now because if I hadn't had help as a young person when I really needed it, I dread to think where I would now be. The death of my dad never goes away. There is a sense of sadness that remains with me but I have learned how to live with it.' –
David Brown

Useful Contacts:

Young Minds
0808 802 5544

Childline
0800 11 11

National Bullying Helpline
0845 22 55 787

Self Injury Support
0808 800 8088

Mind
0300 123 339

CALM (Campaign Against Living Miserably for men aged 15-35)
0800 585858

Family Lives
0808 800 2222

TELL ME WHAT YOU WANT,
WHAT YOU REALLY, REALLY WANT

KNOWING what we want out of life is half the battle. Then we can start to put a plan together to work towards that goal. I bought an inscribed plaque some years ago that has sat in a prominent position in my office ever since. It bears the following words, *'The Perfect Day. Going to Bed With a Dream. Waking Up With a Purpose.'* I get energised at the prospect of new beginnings. I thrive on new challenges. The journey ahead is as exciting as the sense of achievement is satisfying.

It's when we feel lost and rudderless that even the smallest tasks in life can start to feel overwhelming. Then we must go back to a method I described earlier – chunking it down. Look at the next hour. What could we do between now and then that has purpose? Get dressed? Walk the dog? Eat? Ask for help? If this is where we are, self-care must take priority.

In order to work out what it is that we want from our lives we need to have a mental clear out first. If we keep throwing items into the attic, it's just a temporary tidying up solution. And when we go to find something in the attic, it's so muddled that locating that item easily is impossible. Our brain often gets treated the same way. We are all too often guilty of rushing through life, multi-tasking, without any real thought for the bigger picture and where we want to be in a week, month, year from now.

During my illness, I made a some decisions about how I wanted to live my life going forwards, who and what I wanted more of and which areas of my life would be allocated less of me. Just like a spring clean at home, if we are having a mental tidy up, we need to tackle one area at a time, or the task ahead seems exhausting and unachievable.

First, look at your work, voluntary or otherwise. Do you feel shredded at the end of each day and too tired to enjoy your down time? Are you taking work home or working through lunch and not taking a break? Could others help here or do you need to re-negotiate your hours or consider changing jobs?

Next, look at your responsibilities to others. Are you the one who always organises Christmas and is then too tired to enjoy the festivities? Do you do the lion's share of care for elderly relatives? Does worrying about others keep you awake at night or make you restless and irritable during the day? Could you get more help with caring for your young children, from a partner or by sharing a school run with another parent? Do you share your home with others but do all of the cooking and cleaning yourself? Don't be a martyr unless you are happy to feel mentally and physically fried at the end of each day. Which none of us should, by the way. Releasing control over some areas of your life and delegating to others is key here.

Last, look at your free time. How many times do you say yes to an invitation, when you are already tired and desperate to claw back some time for a bath and an early night? Don't be afraid to say no and allocate that time to yourself, in order to revive your energy levels. Are you part of a social group that you see out of duty or habit, rather than because it makes you happy? Is it time to start putting some distance between you?

Don't tackle it all at once. To do this mental tidy up properly, it isn't possible to cover everything over a cuppa. Take one area each week or each month. Make notes, lists, changes. Don't move onto the next area until you have covered the previous one thoroughly and you are happy with your decision making. When you have worked through all these areas and your life has started to regain balance, it's time to look at the gaps.

After allocating time for those close to you, work and activities you enjoy, look at the time that is left. Now you can think about the things you really want to do, that make you smile and write down up to three. It might be a long held ambition to learn a language or play the piano. It might be that you never have time to become immersed in a novel and would like to read more. Perhaps your fitness has been overlooked and you would like to make strides here. Maybe you take your holidays in the same location because you don't have time to think about exploring further. Which activities are your choice and yours alone. All that is important is that they matter to you and make you happy. When you have reached your decisions and written down your top three, allocate time in your newly organised life for the first activity on your list and ring fence that time. The thing you want to do is important for your well-being. Make it matter and stick with it. If you find you don't enjoy your new activity as much as you had hoped, that's ok; you have found that out so the time was not wasted. Or it may be that the first activity is quickly achieved. Go back to your list and move to the next activity and try that. This is your time, to spend exactly as you choose.

Goal setting is a big part of my professional life, as well as being an integral part of my personal development. Whether I am mentoring young people in schools and colleges or working with adult clients at my well-being retreats, in hospital clinics or during personal training, quite often the reason they have become fearful of change is that they have become stuck in a rut and lost sight of what it is they want to achieve. Despite their desire for change, they are also often overwhelmed by what is needed to improve their well-being and unable to start, perpetuating further anxiety or depression. With guidance, each individual isolates their aim and takes one step at a time to move towards it. Keeping a diary can be really useful here, of feelings and of positive steps taken, to measure progress and prove achievement. Each new achievement motivates us to take another step towards our aim. As we reach our original aim, we may find that we have started to recalibrate what it is we want to achieve and set new goals, as we discover a newly found confidence. Each time we do this, we gain control, where this was previously missing. The benefits of small and big wins here are huge. If we can do this one thing, what can we do in other areas of our lives to improve our happiness? When I ask for an aim, the answers have been many and varied and each as important as the last. They have ranged from, *'I want to be a world champion in my sport'* and *'I want to run the London Marathon'* to *'I want to learn to swim in the deep end', 'I want to be able to sleep at night'* and *'I want to stop having panic attacks.'* Don't be afraid to dream big or small. Neither is right or wrong because it's your dream, your aim. Size doesn't matter here.

***

Six weeks into the Coronavirus pandemic, I asked friends, colleagues and clients of all ages and backgrounds and different parts of the world, to choose up to three things that were sustaining them through lockdown, aside from much missed friends and family, as we were largely not able to see and hug those closest to us, unless we lived in the same house or were part of another person's support bubble. This is what they had to say:

Hannah Illman
Dogs, food, fresh air

Siscu Pérez
Coffee, food, sun on our terrace

Sue Gofton
Varied meals, ordinance survey map for our walks

Phil Penfold
My garden, writing, weekly delivery of real ale from local pub

Peni Nolan
Work, garden, cycling

Melanie Salmon
Books, walking, time for reflection

Royston Sinclair
Faith, God, communication

Joanne Howard
Exercise , my dog , wine

Joanne Lawrence Clark
Walking boots, suntan lotion, fence paint to keep busy

Nicole Lampert Brockman
Alcohol, exercise classes, my bike

Joy Chantry
Garden, Kindle, walks

Sally Brockway
Coffee, running, writing

Tanya Mckenzie-Gordon
Exercise, technology, wine

Julie Gilby
Walking, yoga, sunshine

Alan Pleasants
Radio, food, garden

Caren Swift
Zoom, garden, box sets

Pat Summerfield
Daily newspaper, Kindle, garden

Pam Hoad
Zoom exercise classes, walking with my dogs, wine

Kate Hyde
Liquor, my greyhound, hair ties

Darina Jefferson
Coffee, baking. films

Sally Kemp
My garden, walking

Keren Paula Read
Bike, books. gin

Pippa Kelman
Running, sleep, Netflix

Ian Parsons
Alcohol, guitar, mobile phone

Francine White
My Kenwood food processor, sunshine, rubbishy sweets

Julie Bartlett
Exercise, garden, Netflix

Demelza Carroll
Gin, tonic and CrossFit

Sharon Stockley
WhatsApp, Bacardi and tonic, my personal trainer on Zoom

Roger Meads
Walking, my garden

Pippa Nevard
Exercise, relaxation, grapes

Alan Taylor
Computer, WiFi, a wee drink

Susan Wilkinson Cox
Freedom, exercise, learning

Bernice Dennison
Exercise, community spirit, good TV

Janelle Woods
Tea, wine, Amazon

Philip Ide
Running , Pilates, cooking

Susan Woods
Sunshine, garden, walks

Isla Chalmers-Tait
Pets, garden

Michelle Gagie
Gin, music, running

Clare Collings
Exercise, local shops, sun

Eleisha Jane
Prayer, garden, internet

Sandy Stevens
Sunshine, contact with friends & family
by phone, gin and tonic

Fiona Impey
Netflix, vodka, pizza

***

How did you spend the lockdowns? Maybe you were working and had little spare time. Perhaps you were furloughed and suddenly found yourself with empty days and weeks to fill. Those I spoke to, from all walks of life, had much in common. They craved outside space, entertainment, exercise and tasty food or drink. After kicking back initially, most told me they liked their day to have purpose, otherwise one day would drift into the next and make them feel more lost and uncertain which day it was. Exercise was used not just for good physical health but to help manage stress and anxiety levels around everything that accompanied the Covid-19 pandemic, from foreboding news headlines to home schooling. Entertainment, with a good book or a box set, was a useful diversion and a tasty meal or drink was a reward. Intentionally or not, we were all trying to satisfy our five senses, of taste, touch, smell, sight and sound, despite, for the majority of us, our reduced lives.

For me, it meant working from home and getting to grips with new technology in order to do so. No commuting meant I had spare time. Four elements brightened my days. The first was good quality, strong coffee, as suddenly I had time to fill a cafetiere, instead of grabbing a takeaway espresso between clients. I exercised indoors in bad weather and outdoors when the sun shone and was diligent about this. Extra time meant I was able to explore new exercise methods I hadn't previously. I still love a sweaty workout but I'm now also a convert to yoga and sleep more deeply when I practise it.

Next, I set about making our outside space more inviting. I planted a lavender hedge, created a flower bed and built two vegetable patches that I filled with fruit and vegetable plants. I had no previous experience and each area was very much built on trial and error but nurturing these plants and being able to pick food I had grown in my garden was hugely satisfying and still is. Aside from the bounty from my garden, this also meant I was spending more time outside. Vitamin D, produced by our body under the skin, as a reaction to sunlight, was a bonus for my physical health. Vitamin D helps to absorb minerals and protect our bones by regulating the amount of calcium and phosphate in the body. It's these nutrients that keep bones, teeth and muscles healthy. Natural light is important for our mental health, too. During lockdown, those who were shielding indoors, were encouraged by mental health charity Mind to sit by a window for periods during the day, to look outside at the sky, trees and birds, to create a sense of space and reduce feelings of claustrophobia.

Lastly, I dug out some books and asked friends for recipes and taught myself to bake bread, with some attempts more successful than others. As my working life has changed as we emerge from lockdown once more and I have less spare time, this luxurious, time consuming activity has been cast aside for now. But I will definitely revisit it. I loved the small victory of a dough rising, the experiments with yeasts and the stress busting bonus of kneading. Most of all, the smell of baking bread wafting through the house is the sweetest perfume.

Making adjustments to our lives during the pandemic, a time of national restrictions, fear and uncertainty, takes courage and patience. As we move out of lockdown, we have to adjust once more and are naturally cautious. 'It's one of the reasons why we are seeing such resistance to people going back into the office post-Covid lock down,' says consultant psychiatrist Phil Hopley. 'Many of us had been able to work from home and had seen the benefits of being able to do that, saving time on commuting and spending more time with our families.

'Those who were isolating by choice or shielding for medical reasons, and had been at home for longer than their friends and colleagues, have often found it harder still to emerge from their houses. To do so, it's important to return to perspective again. It's useful to look at what we have lost through a new way of operating - socialisation and stimulation are important. A solitary life can make us less able to be creative, to create social connectivity and network. Those things get unconsciously forgotten and we need to dial those back up.'

**

Many of us explored technology that was previously unfamiliar: Zoom, Houseparty, FaceTime and WhatsApp video calls, in order to connect to the world beyond our front doors and remain close, at least technologically, to those we love and care for. We perhaps tried online classes, lessons and workshops and explored new skills or revisited old ones. We joined online communities to enjoy streamed music, poetry, dance and theatre, as live entertainment temporarily ceased in theatres and innovative creatives found new ways to deliver their art. We stood on our doorsteps and clapped for the NHS, nodding and waving at neighbours in our street we may not have noticed very much previously. We found ways of coming together. Being part of a community, however big or small, with a common aim, helped sustain us through a period of isolation.

In the midst of the pandemic, the Dalai Lama, leader of Tibetan Buddhism, had this to say. 'No matter how rich your family is, without community, you cannot survive. We really need a sense of oneness. Taking care of others is actually taking care of yourself. We are social animals and each individual depends on their neighbour. When you think about the difficulties you face in your life, think about the other people who have a similar experience of suffering. We need a keen sense of oneness of humanity, remembering what we have in common with everyone else. You want a happy life. I want a happy life. But I think that aim will not be fulfilled only on the basis of material values.'

This doesn't mean we suddenly have to rush out and join a new social club and find a new army of friends. It's helpful to remember that when we choose the people we want to spend our time with, quality is usually far more important than quantity.

Give thought to what it is you really want from your life and go with that. However big or small your aim, remember that it matters to you and allocate its importance. Make a plan and chunk it down into manageable steps. Give yourself a time frame to achieve each step, so that your plan doesn't drift away from you.

It's useful to remember that at our core, we're not so dissimilar from each other. We all need to stimulate our senses. We all like to reward ourselves. And we all need to have people in our network that we trust completely. It's good to say hello to our neighbour and it's equally good to find time for ourselves. And it's always acceptable to ask for help when we need it.

I Did It My Way

'Thinking back to the deterioration in my previous relationships and job challenges, I've learned that the risks involved in change are smaller than I first thought. But this involves getting over a fear of change. I've tried to consider my own weaknesses and strengths in these situations. Do I need to change things about myself and what do I really want? This has been particularly powerful, as I can end up completely reframing the problem, so that the path forward is more obvious.' –
Mike Hyde

'During 35 years in the fire service, there were many stressful events that I had to deal with, but there was a time when this stress was compounded by both going through a divorce and losing my father in a short space of time. Having close friends to discuss these issues with was priceless. But my personal coping mechanism was running. At work, if I had experienced an unpleasant incident, I would go for a run as soon as I got home, whatever the time. I'd try to get into some pleasant scenery, often my local country park. It really helped me cope and get on with my day.' –
Sam Munns

BE KIND TO YOURSELF

WHEN we are trying to move forwards from a trauma, we can't and shouldn't rush. If we fail to acknowledge the emotional and perhaps physical roller coaster we have endured and how it has affected us, this will almost certainly cause problems for us further along in our lives. And it will absolutely affect our fight or flight responses to any future trauma.

There is no right or wrong time frame here. In the short-term, slowing the pace of our lives, just completing daily tasks and getting through each new day and any required decision making after a trauma is absolutely enough. We may be lacking energy and motivation to do these tasks and need professional help with this phase and the support of others and should seek it with impunity.

As we start to be able to put one foot in front of the other, it's important to establish a place of peace in our minds, in order to move forwards. If we haven't already, we may need to confront what we have been through. It may be that there are no answers to some questions and never will be and we need to find a way to come to terms with this. Again, there is no rush. Move through these phases at your own pace. There are no rules about what you should be doing or how you should be feeling at any point, except that it must feel right for you.

It may help to talk through our thoughts with another person to work towards a peaceful mind here, to gain some clarity and perspective. We may need to accept that there will never be an answer to 'Why?' 'How?' and 'What if?' and we need to reach a place where we stop asking those questions in order to stop torturing ourselves.

As a young woman, I would disguise a painful situation by immersing myself in my work or move to a new area and use the home making of a new property as a project to distract from the hurt. This was a temporary fix but left questions about my response to that trauma unanswered. As wisdom got the better of me in passing years, I tackled difficult situations differently. I now ask myself what it is I need in order to emerge strong and unharmed. I don't rush my next move. It may be that I need a change of scene for a day or two, maybe a week, or longer, to help establish perspective. I may need answers about that situation if they are available or someone to talk it through with, to help me see the whole picture. If the situation concerns another person making me unhappy, I calmly confront them at a mutually convenient time, so that we may part having agreed to disagree. I don't leave words unsaid and I listen to their thoughts and opinions, too. This way, everything that needs to be said and heard, calmly, by both parties, has been addressed. There is no longer an elephant in the room the next time we meet. I don't want to be that person who peers around the corner, afraid of who or what they might find, in my daily life. This approach means I sleep well at night and wake rested and there is no residual anger or guilt.

'When we have experienced a trauma, there is a temptation to turn our attention to something new, which leaves behind the opportunity to go through a full range of emotional responses,' comments consultant psychiatrist Phil Hopley. We sometimes need both. Passion Focussed Therapy is a very interesting area. It means applying kindness to ourselves. It's become a very effective, psychological treatment for a range of problems, including anxiety and depression. We need to take a wiser, kinder approach to ourselves.

'It has also become adopted by a number of athletes. The tradition of training yourself into the ground and having a very combative, punitive approach to training, pushing people into states where they are over trained and developing injuries is less commonplace now. A more conciliatory, flexible approach is often very helpful here.'

***

Feeling ready to confront situations in our lives, in order to understand them better and move forwards is a big step. A counsellor will help guide our thought processes if we are comfortable talking to someone else. When we have reached our peace, we may still be reminded of difficult times, often unexpectedly; in conversations, by hearing a familiar sound, revisiting a place, or inhaling a waft of a fragrance. We will each have our own way of navigating those reminders. None is right or wrong. In time, the pain becomes less sharp and that's ok. It doesn't mean we have any less acknowledgement of what has gone before. It just means we are getting a little stronger.

***

When I raised £5000 for breast cancer research, following my hike up and down Ben Nevis, I was able to allocate the funds to a particular project, through Breast Cancer Care (now Breast Cancer Now). I chose to support a research project at Keele University, which hoped to create a new targeted drug treatment for the type of breast cancer I'd had. Gwyn Williams, Professor of Molecular Cell Biology, kindly invited me to Keele University to meet him and find out more about his project. During our meeting, he asked if I would like to step into his laboratory and look at HER-2 positive breast cancer cells in a Petri dish, under a microscope. With a heady mix of curiosity and anxiety, I agreed that I would. It was an extremely unnerving experience.

I had mentally confronted the treatment I needed for cancer. I was accepting of it and enduring it. I had decided to fight my diagnosis and I was two thirds of the way through three-weekly visits to the chemo ward. Now I found myself face to face with a tiny transparent vessel, that bore cells that had been responsible for turning my life upside down, making my children cry and question whether they would lose their mother and my husband fearful at the prospect of losing his wife and becoming a widower.

This unexpected invitation to the lab was an incredibly powerful one. Until this point, cancer had just been a title for the systemic confusion in my body. Now I was facing my enemy, or at least an enemy with the same molecular make-up as my own. Professor Williams patiently explained how his research stages had been planned and executed and that his theories were proving accurately reflected in his testing methods. He was a beacon of hope for overcoming the devil in that Petri dish and his research had proved that not only was his targeted drug going to work, but his research had very positive implications for other cancers.

Sitting on the train, as I returned to London, then Kent, I had time to reflect. I had hit a new junction in my head. I could either concentrate my mind on the damaging cells I'd seen and how angry I felt towards them or I could think hard about the hope for a kinder targeted drug that Professor Williams' research held. I chose the latter. Where there is hope, there is opportunity. This wasn't a day to learn more about cancer. This was a day about hope.

I caught up with Professor Williams recently, to discuss his latest research project and a breakthrough he and his team have discovered in virology, by examining the human genome, and breaking it down into 3000 million bases. Just let that figure sink in for a minute. He explained that he feels privileged to do the work he does and never loses sight of his long-term goal, which is to provide enough scientific evidence to create new targeted cancer treatments. But he quantifies the wins by explaining that for every breakthrough, there have been months, maybe years of painstaking, patient and sometimes frustrating puzzle solving that has lead down blind alleys, as he gradually builds up knowledge to reach that point. He says, 'Realising I'm the first person in the world to have a bit of knowledge, solving a puzzle that had millions of pieces, which could go on to have wide reaching positive implications for the health of others is quite a kick. But inevitably, the more answers I get, the more questions I have. I never have all the answers all at once. I just keep moving forward, one step at a time, doing the best I can and working with what I have. That is all any of us can do.'

***

Turning a Negative Into a Positive

Addressing the negatives in our lives in order to move forwards, requires a positive action.

First of all, list the top three stressors in your life. This could be aspects of your job, your health or personal life or a mixture of all three.

1.
2.
3.

Take your first stressor and work through the following statements:
  - Am I comparing myself to others?
  - Is this stressor out of proportion, am I catastrophising?
  - Am I taking this personally?
Next, remind yourself of these statements and apply them in turn:
  - I tried.
  - I'm starting every new day with a clean slate.
  - I acknowledge that being positive is a work in progress.
  - I am focussed on today.

When you have finished, take the next stressor and continue until you have completed all three. By identifying each area in turn, the stressors in our lives become less overwhelming and we can start to gain perspective.

***

Pull on Your Armour

When I'm working with clients who have been injured and need to gain physical strength, the first thing we do is assess the damage. Then I look to strengthen the muscles around the weakness, to support the weaker muscular or skeletal structure, allowing it to strengthen over time.

When we are trying to improve our mental muscle, it's useful to acknowledge our weakness, then look for our strengths. This might be that we are good at our job or a good listener, or that we are exercising to release feel good endorphins or eating well to support our body. List three things you are good at on a piece of paper and put these on your fridge door or somewhere you will see them every day. When you get a negative thought about your actions, take a look at these and remind yourself of those things that you are good at and build on these.

If you have been in a vicious, self-destructive existence for a long time, maybe most of your life, change can seem scary and overwhelming. It's never too late to break free from a cycle of negativity. Though you do have to want to do it. Without proper commitment, it won't happen. Others can help. You can pull together an army of positive friends and professional help. You can call on this support network if you start to lose faith or confidence in yourself. But no one can do this for you. This is your journey. But it will also be your win and you can own it. What have you got to lose?

When I am mentoring teenagers in school, I ask them what they think they need to make them happy. In most groups there will be at least one young person who raises their hand and answers, 'Lots of money and a big house, Miss.' I then ask them how much money is enough? Is it a million pounds? Would £2m make them happier? If they have one big house, is that enough to be happy or will they then crave another? Will they want an expensive new car to park on the drive – will that make them happy? How about two cars? I then tell them that if they are loved, have some food in their belly, feel safe, healthy, have a roof over their head, enjoy unbroken sleep and are worry free, this is a life achievement. And it's an accomplishment that not everyone experiences. This doesn't mean that I don't encourage ambition. The opposite is true. We spend a lot of time working on their life goals and putting plans in place to put them on a path to achieving them. I encourage them to reach for the moon. I implore them to travel and learn about the world that they live in and how others live in other cultures, elsewhere on our planet. But I also tell them to never lose sight of what they need to make them happy. And I remind them that this isn't necessarily the biggest house in the neighbourhood, a huge bank account or the fastest car.

- Acknowledge your weaknesses.
- Remember what you are good at.
- Think about what you need to make you happy.
- Commit to change.
- And start taking one step at a time towards it.

***

YOUR FIVE-POINT KINDNESS PLAN

1. DEAL WITH TODAY
On tough days, start by just getting up out of bed and coping with small daily tasks; eating, washing and caring for your immediate dependents. Try to get outside for a short walk, which will release endorphins, inducing positive thought patterns.

2. ACCEPTANCE
Accept that you cannot change the past. It is behind you and you are not going there. Seek professional help here if you feel it would be helpful.

3. COMMIT TO YOU
Do one thing every day that is just for you. Read a book. Listen to some music or a podcast. Run. Paint. It doesn't matter what it is, just that it makes you feel happier.

4. BUILD MENTAL MUSCLE

Start to think about what you want from your life. If you are stuck in a rut of sadness or destructive behaviour or you are not feeling satisfied, seek the help of a trusted friend, counsellor or psychiatrist to help you prioritise here and start building mental muscle. Create an achievable goal for each week. Yes, you may make mistakes along the way but that's alright. It's a risk you are going to have to take but it's one that is well worth taking. You need to break a few eggs to make an omelette. Trying brings its own huge rewards. None of us are perfect.

5. LOOK BACK TO SEE HOW FAR YOU HAVE COME

As weeks turn into months, take a glance backwards, to measure how far you have come. If you have come this far, imagine how much more you could achieve? Already, you are stronger than you realised.

***

I Did It My Way

'As a child I lived with and continually witnessed domestic abuse. My father was violently abusive to my mother, leaving her severely physically disabled. This caused me psychological damage, which has impacted my mental health in adult life. I did not fully recognise the impact until my 30s. I have suffered bouts of depression and some very low times that have felt like an endless struggle. I am on a long journey, still learning how to cope, how to look after myself, and how to respect myself. I persevere with the things I'm good at, even when I don't feel like it or when I feel I'm not doing them well. This gives me a sense of achievement. I run for exercise, track my progress, and set myself goals, which supports my mental and physical health. I eat well. For me, comfort eating is a vicious cycle and a form of self-destruction. It made my depression worse and took a long time to break the habit. Exercise definitely helps to suppress the temptation. And I surround myself only with people who make me feel happy and see my worth. This is easier said than done but it's so important.' -
Amy Buchanan

'I am one of life's worriers and often feel stressed because of this. Discovering mindfulness yoga has helped me a great deal. I usually never give myself permission to switch off my worries but doing this gives me permission to do so. As a result, my mind feels stronger and I can cope with my worries better. Music has also become a huge coping mechanism for me. It can transport me to a different place in my head.' –
Andrea Habergham

Useful Contacts:

Samaritans
116 123

Mind
0300123 3393

Anxiety UK
03444 775 774

CALM (Campaign Against Living Miserably for men aged 15-35)
0800 585858

Refuge
0808 2000 247

National Gambling Helpline
0808 8020 133

Alcoholics Anonymous
0800 917 7650

SLEEP

ONE in three of us suffers from poor sleep, according to studies by the British Sleep Society. The quality of our sleep is affected by the day that has gone before. And how well we sleep will certainly impact how we perform the following day. If we aren't sleeping soundly, our opportunity for rest is disturbed and our energy will slump during our waking hours. This not only alters our mood, motivation, function and concentration levels, it can also damage our health, contributing to heart disease, obesity, depression and diabetes. An occasional night with poor sleep will make us tired and irritable the next day but won't affect our health. However, adopting good sleep hygiene habits can have huge benefits.

Our bodies operate circadian rhythm, which is our body clock of rest and activity. It is our natural 24-hour cycle of physical, mental and behavioural changes, our dips and peaks of energy and is controlled by the suprachiasmatic nucleus in the brain, which feeds into the pineal gland, producing melatonin, to assist sleep. Receptors in the retina, which are light receptors only, not visual, feed to the suprachiasmatic nucleus, which is why we wake up when we see light.

Our behaviour when we are awake can affect how deeply we sleep. There are some common triggers here, including illness, anxiety and poor sleep hygiene, where our senses are over stimulated at bedtime, instead of working towards a state of calm relaxation.

How Much Sleep Do We Need?

Most adults need seven to eight hours of good quality sleep each night to function properly. Some of us will need more and some less. What is important is that however long we need, we make sure that we achieve this. If we wake up tired, we are not getting enough sleep. Quality is more important than quantity here. It's better to get less hours of good quality restful sleep than a long period of broken sleep. Children need more sleep, around nine to 13 hours as they develop and grow and more for babies and toddlers, who average 12 to 17 hours of sleep.

***

Sleep Affects Us in the Following Ways:

Immunity

If we seem prone to catching every cold and flu that's going around, our bed time could be to blame. Prolonged lack of sleep can disrupt our immune system, so we are less able to fend off viruses.

Weight

A lack of sleep could be partially responsible for weight gain. A number of studies have shown that people who sleep less than seven hours a day tend to gain more weight and have a higher risk of becoming obese than those who get seven hours of slumber, because their bodies are producing reduced levels of the hormone leptin, which makes us feel full and increased levels of the hormone ghrelin, which stimulates hunger.

Insulin Levels

In addition to affecting the hormones which regulate our appetite, a lack of sleep also affects our insulin levels, by changing the way the body processes glucose in our food, which the body converts to energy, leading to type 2 diabetes if it remains uncontrolled.

Mental Well-Being

A single sleepless night will make us feel moody and irritable, as our energy levels slump. A continued sleep debt may lead to long-term mental health issues, including anxiety and depression.

Sex Drive

Both men and women who don't get enough good quality sleep, risk lower libidos and a loss of interest in sex.

Heart Disease

Long-standing sleep deprivation has been linked to an increase in heart rate and blood pressure, putting additional strain on our cardiac muscle.

Fertility

Poor sleep can lead to issues conceiving a baby, by reducing the secretion of reproductive hormones.

***

Too many of us turn to sleeping pills, as a quick fix, when a more holistic approach could be of greater long-term benefit, says consultant anaesthetist Dr Peter Venn, founder of the Sleep Disorder Centre for sleep medicine. 'In 40 years of working with patients with disturbed sleep, I have prescribed sleeping pills less than 10 times. I spend my life writing to GPs, explaining that the easiest way to get patients off sleeping pills is to not prescribe them in the first place. I work with a clinical psychologist to establish how and when a patient sleeps and any psychological issues that may be preventing sleep. Sleep is usually damaged by behavioural patterns or deep seated issues buried in the subconscious, which make patients fearful of their bed, concerned that they will revisit these thoughts as they sleep. If low level interventions aren't working, it's worth exploring what else might be preventing sleep happening.'

To Fix Poor Sleep Patterns, Try These Options First -

Be patient and accept that there isn't a quick fix here but it's worth persevering. If you've had months of restricted sleep, you'll have built up a significant sleep debt. Try a variety of options until one or a combination of several, improve your sleep and you feel rested when you wake.

Cease any activities that over stimulate the senses at least one hour before you wish to sleep. Take your phone and other devices and put them on the other side of the room or elsewhere in the house, so that if you wake, you are not tempted to reach for them. Blue light from televisions, laptops, phones and tablets stimulate our brain. Limiting these devices before bedtime allows melatonin, the hormone that makes us sleepy, to increase at night when the sun goes down. It's easy to lose hours scrolling through social media, which can increase anxiety levels. Decide how much time each day you are going to allow for this and stick to it. If you are active on several social media platforms, consider reducing these.

Avoid watching the news, action or horror genre film or television an hour before bed, to give your brain time to slow down and calm before you sleep. If you are prone to worrying about news bulletins, limit the amount of news you allow yourself to watch each day on television or listen to on the radio.

Allow up to half an hour at the end of each day to write down your worries. This means you are acknowledging what is worrying you at a time that suits you. Use a pen and paper rather than a device. This teaches our mind to allocate time for these thoughts, so that they trouble us less during the day or overnight when we are trying to sleep.

Before you sleep, prioritise for the following day. Set yourself no more than five important tasks each day. Make a plan to carry them out. Move on to the remaining tasks the following day. If we have lots to do, this way these tasks seem less overwhelming and we maintain control, which will mean we are less likely to worry about them overnight.

Avoid catastrophising. We can spend a great deal of time asking 'what if?' and worrying about the worse case scenario. Quite quickly, a small problem becomes much bigger than it was initially. This is not preparing for the worst by thinking everything through. This is wasted energy, used to create anxiety around situations that may well not occur. What ifs are theories only, not facts. Write these worries down, acknowledge them and allocate another time to revisit them, by which time you may well discover that they have dissipated.

A warm bath before bedtime – not too hot – will help your body reach a temperature which is ideal for rest.

Mindfulness is an excellent technique to help combat poor sleep. There are a number of apps that can help us with this such as *Headspace* and *Calm*, where we guide our thoughts by simply listening and engaging. Some find this helpful first thing in the morning when they wake, to help calm anxiety during the day ahead. Used at the end of the day, sitting quietly, without interruption, mindfulness can help induce good quality sleep.

Those who suffer from seasonal affective disorder, SAD, find that their mood dips during the autumn and winter months, when there is less daylight. If this is familiar, consider using a light box and programme it so that you wake with warm light, which has been proven to help lift mood.

Make sure your mattress is comfortable, supportive of your spine and replaced at least every 10 years.

Keep your bedroom dark at night. Make sure your curtains are lined with black out material, that will prevent sunlight or street light disturbing your sleep. Ideally it should also be quiet, tidy and kept at a temperature of between 18 Celsius and 24 Celsius. If you are disturbed by noise, consider investing in double glazing or opt for ear plugs as a quicker, cheaper solution.

Get outside every day if possible. Being exposed to daylight improves our mood and helps set our body clock. Go for a walk, get into your garden or park. Any quiet open space will work. If you are unable to get outside, make sure curtains are open and that you are exposed to daylight.

Keep a sleep diary. It may uncover lifestyle habits or daily activity that is contributing to your lack of sleep.

There is more than one reason that it's a bad idea to go to bed on an argument. It will affect our relationship with the other person the following day but it will also damage our rest, as we process heightened emotions before we wish to sleep.

On a day off work or weekend, start by going to sleep when you are naturally tired and waking when you feel naturally ready. You may find that you have already gained over an hour of extra sleep. It may be that you sleep for 10 hours but this will decrease to an average of seven to eight hours as this is repeated.

Avoid stimulants, such as caffeine, energy drinks and alcohol at least two hours before bed time. And don't use these as a pick-me-up the following day. These may boost our energy short-term but can disrupt sleep. It's good practice for our health to reduce caffeine overall, to no more than two cups of tea or coffee per day. Avoid cola and energy drinks as these contain caffeine. Reduce or cut these out of your diet for one month and you are likely to discover that you feel alert during the day and more ready to sleep at night. It may be that cutting out caffeine causes headaches. If so, cut down the amount of caffeine you are drinking more slowly, to avoid this side effect.

Although a couple of glasses of wine in the evening can help us fall asleep, we sleep less deeply after drinking alcohol and feel tired the following day. Try to avoid alcohol before bedtime. The NHS recommends that men and women should not regularly drink more than 14 units a week, which is equivalent to six pints of average strength beer or 10 small glasses of low strength wine. Try to have several alcohol-free days each week. If you are drinking every night out of habit, you binge drink alcohol or your alcohol consumption is increasing, consider seeking help in reducing this amount. Aside from the negative affects on our mood and sleep, alcohol is sugar dense, so this behaviour also negatively impacts our calorific intake.

To encourage a regular sleep pattern, aim to go to bed and wake up at the same time each day. Our body clock and brain will gradually respond to this and encourage us to sleep and wake at these times. While it may seem tempting to try to catch up on sleep by having a long lie in after a bad night of sleep, if we do this on a regular basis, it can disrupt our sleep routine. 'Ideally, we should respond to the body's pressure to want to sleep' says Dr Venn, 'and have this aligned with the body clock. When we fight the body's willingness to sleep, our body clock is affected. Also, the later we get up, the less pressure there is to go to sleep the following night.'

Avoid naps during the day, so that your body is ready to rest at night.

Make time for activities that relax you in the evening. Spend time with friends. Listen to music. Read. Try slow, mindful exercise, like yoga, Pilates or Tai Chi. Being relaxed improves our sense of calm, making us ready to sleep.

Drink more water. Every cell and organ in our body needs water to function. Over two thirds of our body is made up of liquid. Sometimes we feel tired simply because we are dehydrated. We should be aiming for eight tumbler glasses or two litres of water every day. Foods with a high water content, water we have flavoured with fruit and herbs, ie lemons, apples, mint and fruit tea, all contribute towards our water intake and improve our hydration.

Sleep on your side rather than on your back to avoid snoring, which will wake us during the night.

Avoid sleeping pills, which may provide short-term relief but are not a long-term solution for establishing good sleep hygiene.

Some find talking therapies, such as counselling or cognitive behavioural therapy (CBT) can assist achieving a good sleep pattern. These are particularly helpful for tiredness caused by stress, anxiety, depression, insomnia or low mood. Cognitive Behavioural Therapy works by teaching the brain processes to learn how to sleep well again, so that we fall asleep faster, wake less and achieve a better quality of sleep. This way, we wake alert and energised for the day ahead. A GP will be able to refer patients to a suitable practitioner. 'Group CBT is also worth considering,' says Dr Venn. 'It is often helpful for patients to understand that they are not the only person suffering with a loss of sleep and this is reassuring for them.'

***

Daytime Sleepiness

Excessive sleepiness during the day affects our decision making and can be dangerous if we are moving or driving. Measuring daytime sleepiness is a useful marker in identifying poor sleep symptoms. One commonly used scoring system is the Epworth Sleepiness Scale (ESS), created by Dr Murray Johns in 1991. The Epworth sleepiness scale is a questionnaire that assesses the likelihood of accidently falling asleep whilst undertaking eight common daily activities. Consider how likely you are to doze off or fall asleep in the situations below, in contrast to feeling just tired, compared to your usual way of life in recent times. If you are frequently answering yes, speak to your GP about having the ESS test measured clinically and consider being referred to a sleep clinic, which will explore symptoms in detail and test for respiratory dysfunction.

Situation -
- Sitting and reading
- Watching TV
- Sitting, inactive in a public place (e.g. a theatre or a meeting)
- As a passenger in a car for an hour without a break
- Lying down to rest in the afternoon when circumstances permit

- Sitting and talking to someone
- Sitting quietly after lunch without alcohol
- In a car, while stopped for a few minutes in traffic

***

There are a number of conditions that benefit from further clinical investigation -

Sleep Apnoea

This occurs when breathing difficulties lead to interrupted sleep. It happens because the throat narrows or closes during sleep and repeatedly interrupts breathing. This results in a drop in blood oxygen levels which causes us to wake at night and feel exhausted the following day. It's more common if we are overweight. Drinking alcohol or smoking will make the condition worse. Men who suffer from sleep apnoea tend to have lower testosterone levels, which can lower libido.

Upper Airways Resistance Syndrome

This is more common in younger people, who are slim with a small throat and short chin. While sleeping, the throat closes a little, forcing the muscles to work harder to push air through our body, so that we can breathe. This disturbs our sleep, so we wake up.

Insomnia

Insomnia is a term for repeatedly waking in the night and being unable to sleep. You may have insomnia if you find it hard to get to sleep, if you wake several times in the night, if you lie awake unable to sleep, if you wake earlier than you would like and find you are unable to return to sleep or if you feel tired or irritable during the day. Dr Venn adds, 'This is an extremely debilitating condition which exists 24 hours each day. A true insomniac will never nap during the day.'

Restless Legs

Restless legs occurs when you get an overwhelming urge to move your legs, which can keep you awake at night. This may also present as a deep ache in your legs or they might make a spontaneous jerking movement. All of these will disrupt sleep and leave us feeling weary the following day.

Anaemia

Iron deficiency anaemia creates lethargy in our muscles and affects our alertness, disturbing our sleep pattern and causing tiredness. Pregnant women and women with heavy periods are particularly prone to this. But it can also affect men and post-menopausal women. Though it is rare, it is also possible to secrete too much iron and this can lead to disturbed sleep.

Underactive Thyroid

An underactive thyroid gland means you have too little of the thyroid hormone, thyroxine, in your body and this makes us feel tired. Other common side effects of an underactive thyroid include weight gain unexplained in other ways, aching muscles and dry skin. It's most common in women and more likely to occur as we get older. A blood test can determine whether this is present and can be organised by a GP.

Coeliac Disease

This is caused by the immune system's reaction to gluten, which is found in starchy foods including bread, cakes and cereals. Apart from tiredness, other symptoms may include diarrhoea, bloating, anaemia and weight loss. A blood test will help establish whether coeliac disease is present.

Chronic Fatigue Syndrome

Chronic fatigue syndrome, also known as myalgic encephalomyelitis, or ME, is a severe and disabling fatigue that is ongoing. There may be other symptoms, such as muscle or joint pain.

Diabetes

Tiredness is a common symptom of both type 1 and type 2 diabetes. Other key symptoms include feeling very thirsty, peeing at night and weight loss. Both can be managed in different ways, with GP referral to a diabetic clinic.

Anxiety

Having a little anxiety, as part of our fight or flight responses, is a good thing. Some of us have constant uncontrollable feelings of anxiety that are so strong they affect our daily life. This can lead to restless sleep and panic attacks. If we are feeling anxious about a situation in our lives, this can adversely affect our sleep. Anxiety feeds on uncertainty and lack of control. For low level anxiety, we can use simple interventions, such as allowing 20 minutes each day to write down our thoughts. Some are predisposed to being more anxious than others and may need professional help in managing their anxiety.

Depression

Depression drains us of mental energy, making us feel physically tired and unable to function effectively. It can stop us sleeping and cause us to wake earlier or irregularly during the night. Professional help from a counsellor or psychiatrist can help with management here.

Glandular Fever

Glandular fever is a common viral infection that causes fatigue, along with increased temperature, a sore throat and swollen glands. Though most of the physical symptoms can be reduced quickly, fatigue can linger much longer.

Menopause

Sleep can be severely disrupted for women experiencing menopause, resulting in sleepless nights. A combination of hot flushes, where the skin feels hot, then cold and increased anxiety around this, lead many women to find that they are being woken each night and then struggle to get back to sleep. On starting to wake regularly, it can become a habit to lie in bed, wide awake, feeling exhausted and frustrated. Women may find they wake, needing to pull the bed covers off because they feel hot. Then when they are wide awake, the body becomes damp and cold, preventing sleep. Looking at the clock, the mind can become anxious about how little time there is left for sleep. Previously good sleepers find they lose the ability to get any good quality sleep, which leaves them tired each morning and with low mood. As the pattern is repeated, women become more anxious about how much sleep they can hope to achieve. Although physical symptoms of menopause can disturb sleep, the anxiety associated with increased lack of sleep must also be addressed to reach a good resolution and better sleep. A GP can prescribe remedies which can help here. Talking therapies can also prove useful to lessen anxiety associated with menopause.

In addition, there are two types of parasomnias, that occur when we sleep and these can prove confusing and often frightening -

'Parasomnias are likely to have underlying psychological explanations,' explains Dr Venn. 'These could be wide ranging and include one member of a family not talking to another, incidents of violence, PTSD, child sex abuse, a divorce or a change in circumstances. EMDR (Eye Movement Desensitisation and Reprocessing) and psychological investigation can help here.'

REM (Rapid Eye Movement) Parasomnia
This occurs later in sleep and we are likely to wake while it happens and remember it in the morning. Known as Dream Enacting Behaviour, this is typified by acting out vivid, often violent, dreams. Dream Enacting Behaviour is usually accompanied by vocal sounds and sudden sharp arm or leg movements.

Non REM Parasomnias
These are wide ranging and occur in the first few hours of sleep and we will have no memory of them in the morning. Childhood parasomnias, such as night terrors, can reoccur in adulthood when we are experiencing stress. Dr Venn adds, 'There is evidence linking this to neuro degenerative disease, so parasomnias should be explored further.'

Sleepwalking

Sleepwalking means walking outside or in the house or carrying out complex movements when you are not fully awake. Like other non REM parasomnias, this happens when we are in deep sleep, in the first few hours of rest.

Sleep Eating Disorder

This means seeking food at night and having no memory of this in the morning. It may involve turning on an oven or using knives while asleep, so safety measures need to be put in place here.

Sexsomnia

Dr Venn explains, 'This is typically influenced by alcohol and means a partner attempts to arouse a bed partner, with no memory of this the next day. This has led to complex court cases.'

***

Exercise for Better Sleep

If you are feeling tired, exercise may be low on your list of preferred activities but regular exercise makes us less tired. As we improve our heart and lung capacity and stamina, it gives us more energy. Even a short walk will benefit us.
For the best results, choose an activity you enjoy and commit to it. Make time for it and ring fence this time.

If you are feeling tired, still exercise but choose an activity that requires less exertion, eg walking instead of running. Start with a small amount of exercise and small commitment of time and build up gradually, as your energy levels increase. Unless you have any underlying health conditions that would create contraindications to regular exercise, aim to increase your heart rate each time you exercise, to release endorphins, suppressing the stress hormone cortisol, to assist a restful sleep.

If our body is carrying excess weight, it can be exhausting, placing extra strain on our heart, which can make us tired. Regular exercise will help us lose weight and, in doing so, feel much more energetic.

Avoid going to the gym or exercise close to bed time as our bodies and brain will find it harder to relax.

***

Eat Well to Improve Sleep

A good way to keep up our energy throughout the day is to eat regular meals and healthy snacks every three to four hours, rather than a large meal less often. This keeps us satiated and provides enough energy to manage our daily activity and cognitive skills, so that we can think clearly and make good decisions. Eating well also means we can allow our bodies to employ protein we have digested, to repair our bones, muscles and cells, when we are at rest and that our bodies will be capable of processing the food we have eaten.

We should avoid eating within two hours of our bed time. Our body will work hard to process our meal, keeping us awake for longer. Eating a meal that makes us overly full can disrupt sleep, as our body is working hard to digest it when we are at rest.

Our insulin resistance increases at the end of the day, so it's a poor time to have a carbohydrate load because we are least physiologically able to digest and process them. If we are going to have a carbohydrate heavy meal, the further back it is from sleep, the better. Many protein rich foods, including poultry and eggs and other food sources, including milk, oats, bananas, eggs and peanuts, contain the amino acid tryptophan, that causes sleepiness. Carbohydrates make tryptophan available to the brain, which is why we feel drowsy after eating a carbohydrate-heavy meal. Tryptophan is converted first into serotonin, then to melatonin in the brain, secreted in the pineal gland.

Snooze Foods

Certain foods contain the amino acid tryptophan, that causes sleepiness. Proteins from the food we eat are the building blocks of tryptophan, which is why the best bedtime snack is one that contains both a carbohydrate and protein, such as cereal with milk, peanut butter on toast or cheese and crackers, as the carbohydrate element in these combinations makes tryptophan available to the brain.

These foods, vitamins and minerals contain properties which help promote sleep:

Lycopene

This antioxidant is primarily found in red fruits and vegetables. Top sources include guava, watermelon, tomatoes, papaya, grapefruit, red peppers, red cabbage, asparagus and parsley. Antioxidants repair inflammation in the body which aids sleep.

Folate

Top sources include lentils, beans, asparagus, avocado, spinach, broccoli and other leafy green vegetables. The body's production of dopamine and serotonin, which help us sleep, depends on adequate folate.

Selenium

This trace mineral has antioxidant properties and affects thyroid function. If the thyroid isn't working efficiently, this can cause us to wake during the night. Top sources include Brazil nuts, fish, turkey, chicken, beef, and whole grains.

Vitamin C

This is important for renewing and repairing tissue, including enhancing the function of blood vessels, which, when behaving correctly, help us sleep. It's abundant in many fruits and vegetables including peppers, guava, leafy greens, kiwi, berries, citrus fruits, tomatoes and peas.

Cherry Juice

Cherries are high in the sleep inducing hormone melatonin, which assists sleep.

Kiwi

Kiwi fruit have a high concentration of sleep regulating chemical serotonin, which tells our brain that we want to sleep.

Children

Good sleep is important for a child's physical and mental well-being. As they grow, children will need between nine and 13 hours of sleep each night, to allow their bio chemistry to function adequately. The amount of sleep a child needs changes as they get older. A five year old needs about 11 hours a night, for example, while a nine year old needs around 10 hours. Babies and toddlers need more, between 12 and 17 hours.

In order for this level of sleep to occur, it's important to establish a good sleep hygiene pattern as soon as possible, with a relaxing bedtime routine.

Try to do the same things in the same order each night:
- A warm (not hot) bath will help a child relax and get ready for sleep.
- Keeping lights dim in their bedroom encourages a child's body to produce the sleep hormone, melatonin, encouraging a sleepy feeling.
- Once they're in bed, encourage a child to read quietly or listen to some relaxing music, or read a story together.

Avoid keeping tablets, smart phones, televisions and other electronic gadgets in the bedroom, as these can affect how easily children get to sleep. Charge them in another room. Older children may be tempted to stay up late or wake in the middle of the night to use social media. Encourage children to stop using screens an hour before bedtime.

A child's bedroom should ideally be dark, quiet and tidy. It should be well ventilated and kept at a temperature of between 16 Celsius and 20 Celsius.

Fit thick curtains or black out blinds to block out any daylight or street light.

Nightmares and Night Terrors

Many children experience night terrors but most grow out of them. Night terrors are different from nightmares.

Night terrors occur when the child screams or thrashes their limbs and may not recognise you if you comfort them. It happens when awaking abruptly from deep sleep and is common in children aged three to eight years old. The child will not be fully awake and will have no memory of this the next day. They may happen more than once per night. They can be triggered by something that has made them over tired, such as medication or a fever or something that is likely to make them wake, such as anxiety, a sudden noise, a full bladder or excitement. Don't intervene or interact with them. Stay calm and wait for them to settle. Don't attempt to wake the child, as this may agitate them further. When they are calm, ensure they are in a good position to sleep. If terrors persist, discuss with your GP, who will check for any clinical causes that may be affecting their breathing and disturbing their sleep.

Nightmares happen during dream sleep, also known as REM or rapid eye movement sleep and are common aged three to six. The child will wake and may be able to describe the nightmare. Nightmares usually happen late into the night and can cause distress or anxiety. They can be caused by heightened emotion, such as watching a scary film or something that is troubling them. Talk to the child to discover if anything is worrying them and triggering their nightmares. If they are being caused by a stressful experience, they may need counselling. A GP can help organise this.

Teenagers

A minimum of eight to nine hours of good quality sleep is recommended for teenagers.

If a teenager has had a good sleep routine as a child, they may challenge any encouragement to sleep as they get older. In order to promote healthy growth and good cognitive skills, it's just as important in teenage years that good quality sleep occurs.

Encourage teenagers to charge their mobile phones, tablets and other blue screen devices in another room or as far away from their bed as possible, so that they are not tempted to reach for them at night. If they use a screen or television in their room, agree a time when these will be turned off. Better still, keep them in another room, to avoid them interfering with sleep.

Encourage a teenager to have at least 30 minutes of screen-free time before going to sleep.

Encourage a teenager to exercise every day for at least 20 minutes and long enough to get their heart rate up. This will produce dopamine, which will help them sleep later in the day. Exercising in daylight will help the body produce vitamin D, which regulates the amount of calcium and phosphate in the body, needed for healthy bones, teeth and muscles.

Suggest that a teenager drinks less caffeine, found in energy drinks, cola, tea and coffee. These should be avoided altogether after 2pm. Too much caffeine can stop them falling asleep and reduce the amount of deep sleep they have.
Let teenagers know that eating too much, or too little, in the evening, can lead to an overfull or empty stomach. Both can be a cause of discomfort during the night and may prevent sleep.

Ensure that a teenager has a good sleeping environment, which should ideally be a room that is dark, not too warm, quiet and comfortable.

Talk to a teenager about anything they are worried about and keep the conversation going. If they are comfortable talking to you at other times, they are more likely to share their worries. By helping to put these worries into perspective, a teenager is likely to sleep better. Encourage them to write down their worries or to make a list of jobs to do the following day, before they go to bed. This should mean they're less likely to lie awake worrying during the night.

Encourage a teenager to not sleep late for hours at weekends. Late nights and long lie-ins can disrupt their body clock and leave them with weekend sleepiness on Monday morning.

***

I Did It My Way

'I work in London and the commute to my job in winter is a particularly hard time for me. It's cold and dark when I leave for work in the morning and I come home in the dark, too. Winter feels like it stretches on forever and the days seem longer than they do when the sun is shining. To cope with this, I go mountain biking at the weekends. In that small amount of time, I feel free. I can go wherever I want, doing something that lifts me. Even if it's only for an hour, I enjoy every minute of it. I don't worry about anything when I'm on my bike. It's my time to escape. When I come home, I feel much more positive. It's great for my mental health as well as my fitness.' –
Ashley J Dean

Useful Contacts:

British Sleep Society
01543 442 156

Diabetes UK
0345 123 2399

Coeliac UK
0333 332 2033

EXERCISE FOR A VITAL YOU

MOVING is what humans are designed to do. Regular movement stretches our muscles, enabling us to walk, run, jump, twist, bend, stretch, push and pull. If we are sat in the same position for prolonged periods, at a desk or behind the wheel of a car, our bodies adapt to this behaviour, shortening our muscles, tightening our hamstrings. For those with a largely sedentary life, regular exercise to prevent injury is vital.

Exercise also fuels our engine, improving our heart and lung function and digestion, creating an energy base for functional fitness, so that we can complete everyday tasks easily, with confidence and without hesitation and we can run to catch a train without needing 10 minutes to recover.

In addition to the physical benefits, exercise can play an important role in managing our mental health, helping us focus, process thought and make decisions, by releasing calming chemicals in the brain. When our brain reaches a state of calm, we sleep more easily and wake rested in the morning, ready for the day ahead.

Consultant psychiatrist Phil Hopley explains, 'When we exercise, a number of different processes get triggered. Exercise releases endorphins, which are a naturally occurring chemical which have antidepressant properties. That's why people talk about feeling better after exercise. There is a raft of research that supports the evidence base for exercise as a strategy for good mental health but also as an effective treatment for people with mild to moderate depression and anxiety. DNA testing can determine whether the brain derived neurotrophic factor (BDNF) gene is present in a gene combination that makes some of us more susceptible to these conditions. People who have a certain combination of BDNF genes will benefit substantially more than others, from the impact of exercise. It's staggering the improvement in mental state without the use of antidepressants for these people'.

He adds, 'The human wants to learn while moving. Bright sparks will have meetings which are mobile, maybe walking or running, as the brain seems to process better while we're moving. Presumably this is because that is how we lived centuries ago. We were on the move. We make clearer decisions when we are moving. Movement seems to free us up from some of the mundane mental processes that might get in the way in daily life. Run and you will think more clearly than when you are walking around the supermarket.   It's when we can be more creative, too.'

***

When I felt physically weak during my cancer treatment, the mental battle that accompanied that diagnosis became far harder to bear. By exercising whenever I felt able to, I reassured myself that my body was not just coping but winning, which made me mentally stronger. When I couldn't drive to the gym, I would walk to my village shop to buy a newspaper. On an average day, this takes no more than 10 minutes. On my first walk to the shops after reconstruction surgery, it took 25 minutes to get there and 25 minutes to get home again, exhausted and needing to sit down. The following day, I would try again and aim to reduce my time. By walking to the shop every day, my heart and lung function improved and my muscles grew stronger. As time for the walk decreased, I became not just physically stronger but mentally resilient, too.

When I put a weight on my back in the gym, the day after the soul destroying conversation with my children about my diagnosis, I felt weak and beaten. By persevering and adding weight, I reminded myself that my body was strong and capable and this reassurance made the mental endurance test that cancer delivered, easier to manage. Phil Hopley adds, 'In this action, you are then showing yourself the old phrase, fake it until you make it. You can do a bit more than you think.'

Every 18 months I have a DEXA bone density scan. The drugs I take to prevent further cancer cells forming now, have the side effect of tiredness and weakening bone density. The scan checks that my bones are still within normal range. When I had my first baseline DEXA scan, some of my bones were presenting as osteopenic, weaker than they should be. My oncologist wanted to prescribe a course of calcium tablets. I made a deal with her that I would do all I could with diet adjustments and bone strengthening, weight bearing exercise to rectify this. If I was re-tested a year later and still presenting as osteopenic, I would agree to take the pills, and she agreed. I set about increasing the calcium content in my diet and added to the amount and variety of resistance training in my exercise regime. A year later, still taking the drugs with the side effect of weakening bones, my DEXA scan showed that my bone density was back in normal range and it has remained so with every repeated scan. Would this have happened with diet alone? It's highly unlikely. Would it have happened had I exercised without supporting my workouts with the correct calcium rich dietary fuel? I very much doubt it. By allowing exercise and nutrition to work together, we create the perfect storm for our bodies to respond to and overcome the most difficult of tasks.

***

Find the Right Exercise for You

Exercise will only be sustainable if you are enjoying it. To establish all round fitness and to prevent both boredom and injury, I vary my exercise. In a typical week I'll do two workouts that combine high intensity interval training (HIIT) that drive up my heart rate and challenge my lung capacity and resistance work for bone and muscle density. I'll add a dance lesson and a yoga session to maintain good posture and core strength and I'll go for a run or a long hilly walk. I'll do some exercise alone and some with friends. When I was younger, I would train HIIT more often and run more. As I get older, I'll change my workouts again to suit my physiology. I can't imagine my life without exercise. It's a great reassurance that my body is strong and capable and a very effective stress buster.

I train clients of all ages and abilities. My oldest client is 82 years-old and has astounding stamina and strength. He has overcome a heart condition to play tennis twice a week and is active daily, walking everywhere he can. He has exercised all his life and consistency is key. If you want to improve your overall fitness and invest in a healthy future, make a true commitment to it. Ring fence time in your diary for exercise and don't change your plans. Maybe arrange to exercise with a friend, so you are less likely to back out of your planned session. Consider joining a sports team or club, where you will meet others who enjoy the same sport and encourage each other.

Consider your motivation. Who are you exercising for and why? Do you want to feel fitter and stronger or are you trying to change shape to please or impress someone else? In my experience as a personal trainer, long-term change is only ever sustainable and successful if you are motivated to change your biomechanics to please yourself. When I work with clients, I measure their fitness every three months under test conditions and monitor their nutrition and exercise in the meantime, gradually increasing intensity. I measure their bodies to prove that they have changed shape and reduced body fat, as they may not be noticing day to day that they are becoming leaner. The scales are used as an occasional check only. Women, in particular, can become fixated by weighing scales and horribly demotivated if they don't read as they hoped. There are so many variants that can apply here to affect our weight, including hormonal changes and muscle density.

When you are setting a fitness goal, make sure that it is achievable and realistic. So many of us, women in particular, spend a great deal of our lives striving to be what we perceive to be the 'perfect' size. If you are healthy and fit, with strong muscle and bone density, you are eating well, and committed to regular exercise, your body will reward you much more richly than any perceived 'perfect' size ever will.

***

Our muscles are triggered in different ways by aerobic and anaerobic exercise and we should include both for optimal fitness.

Aerobic Exercise

Any exercise that is maintained for a period of time, increases our heart rate and the body's use of oxygen, can be described as aerobic exercise. Faster breathing and heart rate will increase blood flow to the muscles, strengthening the body's cardiovascular system.

Circuit Training

This is a steady form of interval training which will usually include both high energy movement, such as running, with weight bearing exercise using body weight and a combination of devices, that might include kettlebells, body bars, barbells or dumbbells.

Dance Aerobics and Zumba

Dance aerobics and Zumba are fun, high energy workouts that require some co-ordination, and usually take place in a dance or gym studio.

Spin
Spin classes use a static bike to work the legs and glutes, by alternating pace and resistance, improving core strength by maintaining a strong position.

Combat
This is a high energy class of martial arts moves to music, usually involving explosive movement and some core activity at the end of the class.

HIIT

High Intensity Interval Training (HIIT) works by exercising continuously and intensely, moving for short bursts of time, with short rest periods in between. Tabata training, using 20 seconds of activity and 10 seconds rest, works similarly.

Running

Running or jogging at a steady pace will work leg and glute muscles and is at its most effective when the pace and landscape alters, to include sprints (anaerobic) and hills.

Cycling

Like running, cycling should be maintained at a steady pace and incorporate sprints and hills for maximum aerobic and anaerobic benefit.

Interval Training

Interval training is any exercise that is repeated for a period of time with intense bursts of activity and short periods of rest.

***

Anaerobic Exercise

Anaerobic exercise is delivered in short, intense bursts and includes sprinting and weight lifting.

Strength

Strength and resistance training can take many forms and helps us create dense muscle tissue, which assists in burning calories, improving our metabolism. Weight lifting will improve our arm and leg strength and is at its most effective when the core muscles are fully engaged.

Aerial

Aerial classes such as hoop, pole and trapeze use body weight and require good core strength.

Body Weight Exercise

Strength training using body weight, with movements such as press ups and stress holds such as wall sits, will test our body strength without the need for equipment. This is particularly useful at home or when travelling. Add a resistance band to increase intensity.

***

Core Strength

By training our core muscles, we underpin every other exercise we do. When our core muscles are switched on, they impact our posture, helping prevent injury and making both aerobic exercise and weight bearing exercise more effective. For our core muscles to be firing correctly, we need to control our breathing, taking a breath out on exertion and a breath in on recovery. Learning to adjust our posture and control our breathing also helps with stress and anxiety. There are a number of classes which assist with these techniques.

Pilates

Created by anatomist Joseph Pilates, this practice uses targeted exercise to improve strength, flexibility and posture. Variations include mat based classes and Pilates using a reformer machine.

Yoga

Yoga unites breath, body and mind, to create core strength and a meditative state. There are variants here, including hatha, ashtanga and yin yoga, which move at different speeds and hold poses for different lengths of time. Often yoga classes will combine elements of each.

Tai Chi

Originally developed as a martial art in 13th century China, Tai Chi works with the mind and body, combining deep breathing and relaxation with flowing movements.

***

Exercising Outdoors

There are huge benefits to taking our exercise outdoors. As well as the benefit of movement in a new environment, creating variety, we will gain a blast of vitamin D, created in our bodies as we react to daylight. We may have to work harder at breathing, depending on the weather conditions, which stimulates our cardiovascular system. Phil Hopley adds, 'Light primes us for activity. Our brain is stimulated by light. Our circadian rhythm, the natural biorhythm and energy of our day, is affected by light, so exercise outdoors suits us. Our energy level is naturally high in the morning, tends to dip down in the afternoon and pick up early evening and dip at night time and it makes sense to plan our exercise according to this, if possible. If we exercise in a green space, we reconnect with nature which has a calming effect on our brain, too.' As well as taking your usual exercise outdoors, consider an outside sport you have not have tried before; trail running, rowing, surfing, stand up paddle boarding, tennis, cricket, netball, swimming or exercising on sand for greater resistance.

***

How to Start to Exercise

First and most importantly, choose a form of exercise that you think you will enjoy and stick to. Next, do your research. Speak to an instructor or a friend who does the same sort of exercise, so that you know what to expect and how to prepare. Consider whether you have any health or muscular skeletal conditions that might be affected by exercise. If so, contact your doctor or seek reassurance from a chiropractor or osteopath, who will assess your readiness for exercise. Go along with an open mind. Don't expect too much of yourself. If you are joining a class, don't worry about what anyone else is doing. Exercise is a great leveller. Everyone does it for their own reasons. If other people are moving faster or slower or lifting heavier or lighter weights or maintaining stress holds for longer or shorter periods of time, it really doesn't matter. You are your only competition. If you find you don't like this exercise, your time hasn't been wasted as you now know that you are better suited to something else, so try another form of exercise instead.

***

Avoiding Injury

The simplest way to avoid injury is to work within your known physical limitations or to work with a qualified coach, who will safely push you out of your comfort zone, so that your body can achieve more. If you are exercising for the first time or revisiting exercise after a long time away from training, start slowly and build up. Don't feel pressurised by what anyone else around you is doing. This way, your muscles and cardiovascular system will respond safely, allowing you to exercise more intensely as you build stamina.

***

DOMS

Delayed onset muscle soreness (DOMS) is an ache in the muscles, which is typically felt the day after exercise and can last for three days. It should not last longer than this. DOMS occurs if you are trying a new form of exercise, utilising your muscles in a different way than you would in your usual training or if you are new to exercise. It is temporary and can be helped in the following ways:

Hydration

We lose fluid and electrolytes when we exercise, through sweating, so it's important to replace these. Make sure that you are sufficiently hydrated before you exercise and drink water afterwards.

Massage

To ease muscle soreness, have a sports massage or use a foam roller to gradually ease aching muscles.

Active Recovery

Sitting still encourages the muscles to seize further. Active recovery is more useful. This means exercising to a lesser degree. A run or cycle at a gentle pace or a rowing machine set with reduced resistance can help here.

***

Over Training

Good exercise methodology involves establishing a healthy, balanced relationship between exercise, nutrition and recovery. We need to eat well, in order to fuel our bodies to exercise, creating lean muscle tissue and dense bones. We must allow our bodies sufficient rest before we exercise again.

In all three areas, quality matters far more than quantity. Over training will disturb how our nutrition is processed, creating deficits in energy. We may feel we need to rest more. If we don't respond to this signal and continue to train, we risk injury, requiring a period of recovery, disabling our exercise plan. Train smarter, not longer. For an amateur athlete, a good rule to abide by is two to three days of exercise, depending on intensity, and one day off, repeated.

***

When Should I Exercise?

It's smart to exercise when we have peaks of energy. Working with our body's circadian rhythm, this means exercising in the morning or early evening, when we have the most energy. Try not to exercise too close to bed time, as stimulating activity at this time means it will take longer for us to fall asleep.

***

Mobilising and Stretching

Mobilising

Our muscles need to warm up with low level movement in order to become pliant and able to withstand stress. If we start exercising without doing this, we risk injury.   It's smart to warm up all of our muscles, from ankles to neck, so that we can move easily and without hesitation, making efficient use of our exercise time.

Stretching

When we exercise, we put our muscles under stress and they react by tightening. If we leave them in this stressed state, we encourage delayed onset muscle soreness (DOMS) and injury. We should never stretch our muscles before we exercise, only afterwards, when they are warm. Stretching after exercise will reduce DOMS and prevent injury.

***

What Equipment Do I Need?

You can exercise with little or no equipment, depending on what you want to achieve. You will improve your cardiovascular system by increasing your pace of movement, through any combination of running and jumping. Or join a formatted class online or at a gym.

If you wish to increase muscle density with resistance training, the range of equipment available is vast. If you have space for a home gym, you might want to invest in a bar and plates of varying weights and a resistance specific personal training session to learn how to deliver lifts safely. There are also a wide range of machines available to assist with back, leg and shoulder strength. However, for beginners, a lot can be achieved with a mat, two dumbbells and a kettlebell of challenging weight, suitable for your ability. Again, invest in a personal training session to safely learn a combination of movements or join a class.

***

Will Weight Training Make Me Bulky?

Resistance training will create definition in your muscles, making them lean and efficient but it will not make you bulky. I often hear 'I don't want to look like a body builder.' Competing body builders spend years training in a very specific way to achieve their look. For most of us, concentrating on fat loss and toning our muscles will improve our fitness levels and overall health.

***

What Should I Wear?

If you are returning to or new to exercise, don't concern yourself with investing in a whole new wardrobe of sportswear. Wear clothes that are loose and comfortable enough for you to move in easily. However, do wear trainers that will cushion and support your feet and protect your spine from any explosive movement.

***

Am I Too Old To Exercise?

The short answer to this question is no. Consider the type of exercise that will suit you best and make you happy. Speak to a fitness coach that specialises in that exercise to get more information. If you have any underlying health issues, speak to your doctor before starting to exercise and be clear about these with your fitness coach, who will be able to advise about suitable movement, modifying exercises for you, where necessary.

***

Should I Exercise If I Am Pregnant?

Many women exercise successfully through their pregnancies. If you have exercised previously and your body is used to exercise, continue to do so, modifying movements where necessary. If you haven't previously exercised, don't start a new exercise regime during pregnancy. Speak to a fitness coach, who will advise which exercise is most suitable and changes that you can make as pregnancy progresses. Every pregnancy is different and you should only exercise if it is completely safe for you to do so. Take the advice of your doctor or midwife, who will tell you when exercise should stop.

***

Exercise for Fat Loss

Too many people obsess about weighing themselves on scales. Remember to also consider how your clothes are fitting. Measure your chest, waist and hips regularly and monitor changes here. Ask a fitness professional to monitor your body fat, so that you can see this decreasing as you exercise and eat well. The scales can be affected by many factors, including hormonal changes and an increase in muscle mass. They are a guide but do not tell the whole story and can be devastatingly demoralising if they don't read as you had hoped. Aim to eat well, exercise regularly and to be strong. If you do these three things, your body shape will change accordingly. If you are overweight for your height and you follow these protocols, your weight will decrease.

***

Consistency

Make a plan for exercise and stick to it. Consistency and commitment will pay huge dividends with your overall fitness and well-being. Take a look at your diary each week. Find the gaps. Ring fence that time for exercise and don't change it unless you absolutely must.

Being consistent with your exercise will also make exercising easier. When you move regularly, you start to store 'muscle memory' and repeating those movements next time is less arduous as your muscles adapt to them. When we have a long break between exercise sessions, our muscles and cardiovascular system have to move from their rest phase back to movement, making exercise seem harder.

***

Rest Days

Whatever your exercise level, from amateur to professional athlete, rest days are vital, to allow our stressed muscles time to recover before we start training them again, preventing over training and injury.

Enjoy these and do not feel guilty about them. Amateur athletes should think about exercising for 2/3 days depending on their level and the type of exercise they undertake, then take a rest day before resuming training. We can use rest days for active recovery, which might mean a long walk or gentle bike ride.

Continuing to exercise without rest means that we gradually deplete our strength and are unable to train as effectively as we might wish.

***

Exercising Pre-op and Post-Op

Using exercise and nutrition to prepare for surgery and to assist recovery, for muscular skeletal conditions is to be encouraged. Apply sensible methodology here, exercising parts of the body which are largely unaffected and only exercising on the advice of your doctor. If surgery is for a systemic condition, take the advice of your doctor as to what can safely be achieved.

Any exercise that promotes movement of blood and oxygen around our bodies will help prepare for anaesthetic and assist with cell repair post-op. Always seek the guidance of a fitness professional with specialist skills in this area, who can provide an exercise routine which is safe to follow.

Lastly, set a deadline, so that your goal is time specific and work towards that date. Gwyn Williams, Professor of Molecular Cell Biology at Keele University, says, 'Setting and achieving exercise goals has enormous psychological benefit in helping patients cope with illness. There is no doubt about that.'

***

Food and Exercise

The fittest of athletes will fail to perform well if they are not eating to support their bodies. If your body is given the correct fuel and is hydrated, it will do as we ask. If we have failed to put enough fuel in or eaten a meal that is hard to digest, it has to work twice as hard and again, will fail to give its optimum output. If we eat too much sugar, our bodies will enjoy a short burst of energy but this energy will slump after we hit our insulin peak. Think about when you are exercising. Ensure that you have eaten well and stopped eating at least an hour before you exercise, so that your food has digested and its energy has distributed through our body. Eat a protein rich meal afterwards, to repair stressed muscles.

***

Setting Goals and Measuring Fitness

Without a goal, it's easy to lose motivation for exercise. Firstly, consider what your goal is. Choose something specific, such as achieving fitness for a race or being able to wear an item of clothing or complete a task quicker, such as a distance run. I set a fitness test for each of my clients and repeat this every three months for 12 months, then change the test as their fitness levels increase. With every test, their improved fitness will be reflected in their fitness test, as they complete more rounds or finish it faster than last time. Set new goals as your own fitness improves, to keep you challenged and motivated.

Make sure your goal is achievable. I am a big believer in aiming high and that everything is possible with the right amount of commitment and training. Consider how much time you have to commit to your fitness and choose your goal accordingly.

***

Believe in Yourself

If you are doubting your body's ability to exercise, or achieve new exercise goals, remember that everyone had to start from zero at one point. During my cancer treatment, every time I had a new dose of chemotherapy or another surgery, my body had to repair and start building up all over again. Fuel your body correctly.

Listen to it and let it rest when it needs to. Refuelled and revived, believe in your body and notice how your confidence grows as your fitness increases. Don't compare yourself to others. Their journey is important to them but it isn't yours. This is all about you and your wins.

***

I Did It My Way

'The most stressful time of my life was when I was diagnosed with cancer. As someone who goes to the gym regularly and keeps fit and active, always cooks fresh and from scratch, including loads of fruit and vegetables, has never smoked and is only a social drinker, it came as a bit of a shock. My first thoughts were why me? I was given a 17 per cent chance of survival. I decided to do all those little jobs that never get done and sort out as much as I could so that my family would be ok. I also kept up with the gym, going for walks and riding my bike as I knew I would need to be fit to get through the coming months. The treatment, which included chemotherapy and surgery, was intense. There wasn't a moment to forget about what I was going through. I went back to the gym as soon as I was able to and was amazed at the support from all my gym buddies. For something to focus my training on, my daughter signed me up for the cycle leg of a team triathlon, with her and her partner, which was a great motivator for my fitness. Four years after the operation and I am still cancer free. Embrace all the support you are given by family and friends. Stay positive, exercise, eat well and fight as hard as you can for your life.' – **Roger Meads**

EXERCISE ROUTINES

FIRST and most importantly, commit to your exercise and stop finding excuses. Trust me, I've heard them all. Be consistent. Aim to move three times a week for 30 minutes minimum. Build from there. Don't do 10 sit ups, check the scales and wonder why you haven't dropped a dress or shirt size.

The exercise programs I have designed here vary in intensity. Some are easier, others are more challenging. Many of the exercises can be modified. For instance, mountain climbers against a wall are easier than mountain climbers on the floor. Modify where necessary, using my exercise guide and select workouts that reflect your energy level, ability and agility. If you are short on time or energy, choose a shorter workout. If you are feeling strong and energised, choose a more challenging workout and move for a longer time.

These workouts revolve around 26 moves that cover all muscle groups and require little or no equipment. The kit items I have selected: dumbbells (hand weights), mat and skipping rope are inexpensive and easily available. If you don't have them, improvise with household items that you can safely utilise. If you don't have hand weights, try water bottles filled with water or sand, according to your required resistance.

Some workouts are cardio heavy, others focus more on resistance training and some concentrate on core strength. Many are a mixture of all of these. For the best results, be sure to include all these options in your training. This way, your cardio vascular system will reward you, your muscles will gain definition and your bones will increase in density.

Include some core strength exercises every week. The stronger your core muscles become, the more effective your other exercises will be. Your running style will improve as you hold your posture better and you will be able to lift heavier weights as your core better supports your lumbar spine.

I feel energised when I play music during exercise, whether this is a work out or a run. Put a playlist together than inspires and invigorates you.

If you are coping with illness or injury, take medical advice before doing exercise. If exercise is new to you, start slowly and build up, gradually increasing the length of time you exercise and the intensity. Aim to work for a minimum of 20 minutes and a maximum of 45 minutes, including warm up and stretch. If you have upper body issues, stay with leg exercises. If you have lower body issues, build upper body and core strength while seated or laying down, within your capability. If you can't run, jog or walk.

If you have no medical impairment and have exercised before, train for up to an hour each time, giving each session everything you've got. Make the most of the time you have allocated to improve your strength, endurance, stamina and flexibility and leave nothing in the locker. Use weights that will challenge you, but can be lifted safely.

Whatever your level, always go for good form over high reps. Take as many breaks as you need and move at your own pace.

This is your time to make a difference. Don't waste it.

***

Warm Up

Always warm up before exercise and stretch your muscles after your workout. Do each of these actions for at least 15 seconds. Start with a jog on the spot, gradually increasing speed. Bring your knees up in front of you. Return to a jog on the spot. Kick your heels up behind you. Return to a jog on the spot. Rotate your hips in big circles. After five rotations, change direction and repeat. Roll your shoulders. Rotate your arms, gradually lifting your arms higher, until your elbows sweep past your ears. Repeat, taking your arms in the opposite direction. Turn your head so that you can see your right shoulder. Bring your head back to a neutral position. Then, turn your head so that you can see your left shoulder. Return your head to a neutral position. Look up to the ceiling, then down to the floor. Return your head to a neutral position. Take your right ear towards your right shoulder, then your left ear towards your left shoulder. Return your head to a neutral position. If the warm up presents no pain, continue with your exercise. If you have tight muscles, visit a physio or sports massage therapist to help these ease.

***

Learn the Moves

These are the exercises that you will find in my workouts. There are, of course, dozens more to discover as you progress, and many combinations of these. Make sure you familiarise yourself with the technique of each exercise in a workout meticulously before you complete it, so that your training is safe and effective. Do not exceed your current ability level. Only increase your exercise intensity when your body is fully ready to do so. Accept that day to day progress will be gradual and play the long game for lasting results. Take your time and work with your body, not against it. Remember to take rest days and avoid over training to minimise risk of injury.

***

Burpee

1. From a standing position, feet hip width apart, place both hands on the floor in front of you, either jumping or stepping your feet behind you, then lowering your body to the floor. Facing the floor, your whole body must make contact with the floor.

2. Either step or jump your feet towards your hands and return to a standing position. Make a small jump and clap your hands together overhead.

Half Burpee

1. From a standing position, feet hip width apart, place both hands on the floor in front of you, either jumping or stepping your feet behind you, so that you are on the balls of your feet.

2. Facing the floor, either step or jump your feet towards your hands and return to a standing position. Make a small jump and clap your hands together overhead.

High Knees

1. Stand with feet shoulder width apart.

2. Alternating your legs, bring your knees up towards your waist. Improve your speed if you wish to make this harder.

Lateral Raise

1. Stand with feet shoulder width apart. Keeping your arms at your sides, shoulders relaxed. Hold a dumbbell in each hand, with your wrists facing your thighs.

2. Take a breath in and exhale as you raise the dumbbells to shoulder height. Keep your core muscles engaged, ensuring not to arch your back. Take a breath in as you return the dumbbells to start position.

Forward Lunge

1. Stand with feet shoulder width apart. Put your hands on your hips. Take your left foot a full stride length in front of the right, lowering the right knee to the ground. Your left heel should be firmly planted on the ground.

2. Push through the left heel to draw your right leg up to a standing position. Repeat with alternate legs coming forwards. Your feet should remain hip distance apart.

Reverse Lunge

1. Stand with feet shoulder width apart. Put your hands on your hips. Take your left foot a full stride length behind the right, lowering the left knee to the ground. Your right heel should be firmly planted on the ground.

2. Push through the right heel to draw your left leg up to a standing position. Repeat with alternate legs moving backwards. Your feet should remain hip distance apart.

Mountain Climbers

1. With your feet hip width apart, place your hands on the floor, beneath your shoulders, spreading your fingers.

2. Keeping your back flat, bring your left knee into your chest. Replace your left foot as you bring your right knee to your chest. Alternate knees to chest.

Mountain Climbers Against a Wall

1. With your feet hip width apart, take your weight to the balls of your feet and place your hands on the wall in front of you, at shoulder height, spreading your fingers.

2. Bring your knees close to the wall, alternately raising your left and right knees.

Press Up

1. Start with your hands on the floor, beneath your shoulders, arms straight and your feet hip width apart. Lower your chest to the ground, keeping your elbows close to your sides and abdominal muscles engaged. Keep your body straight, from head to feet.

2. Press your hands to the floor and straighten your arms, lifting your body, until your body returns to your start position.

¾ Press Up

1. Start with your hands on the floor, beneath your shoulders, arms straight and your knees on the floor, hip width apart. Take your weight into your legs, just above the knee, avoiding the knee joint. Lower your chest to the ground, keeping your elbows close to your sides and abdominal muscles engaged. Keep your body straight, from head to coccyx.

2. Press your hands to the floor and straighten your arms, lifting your body, until your body returns to your start position.

Shoulder Press

1. Stand with feet shoulder width apart. Keeping your arms at your sides, shoulders relaxed, hold a dumbbell in each hand, with an over hand grip. Raise the dumbbells to shoulder height, palms facing forwards.

2. Take a breath in and exhale as you continue to lift the dumbbells overhead, until your arms are straight. Take a breath in as you return the dumbbells to shoulder height. Repeat. Engage core muscles and do not arch your back.

Jumping Squat

1. Stand with feet shoulder width apart. Hold your hands in front of your chest. Push your hips backwards, widening your knees, keeping your chest upright and forward facing.

2. Continue to bend your knees and lower your body, until the top of your hips pass just below the top of your knees. Keeping your heels in contact with the floor, push through your feet and jump upwards. Repeat.

Air Squat

1. Stand with feet shoulder width apart. Hold your hands in front of your chest. Push your hips backwards, widening your knees, keeping your chest upright and forward facing.

2. Continue to bend your knees and lower your body, until the top of your hips pass just below the top of your knees. Keeping your heels in contact with the floor, push through your feet and return to an upright position.

Squat Thrust

1. With your feet hip width apart, place your hands on the floor, beneath your shoulders, spreading your fingers, in an extended arm plank position.

2. Keeping your back flat, jump both feet towards your chest and then return to an extended arm plank position. Repeat.

Tricep Extension

1. Stand with feet shoulder width apart. Keeping your arms at your sides, shoulders relaxed, hold a dumbbell in each hand, with an over hand grip. Raise the dumbbells to shoulder height, palms facing forwards.

2. Continue to raise the dumbbells until they meet overhead and your arms are straight. Take a breath in and bend your elbows, taking the dumbbells behind your head. Exhale as you raise the dumbbells to meet overhead. Repeat. Adjust the dumbbell weight or use one dumbbell if two are too heavy for you to move with control. Engage core muscles and do not arch your back.

Walk Out

1. With your feet hip width apart, place your hands on the floor, beneath your shoulders, spreading your fingers.

2. Walk your hands forward to an extended arm plank position. Walk your hands back towards your knees and stand upright. Repeat.

CORE EXERCISES:

Crunches

1. Laying on the ground, facing upwards, keep your feet together, heels on the ground and toes facing upwards, and rest your fingers at your temples.

2. Keeping your heels on the ground, engage your core muscles, tuck your chin into your chest, take a small breath in and exhale as you lift your shoulders off the floor. Keep your eyes focussed on your knees, to stop your head falling backwards. Keeping your chin tucked into your chest, return your shoulders to the floor, taking a small breath in. Repeat.

Bicycle Crunches

1. Laying on the ground, facing upwards, keep your feet together, heels on the ground and toes facing upwards, and rest your fingers at your temples.

2. Lifting your heels off the ground, engage your core muscles, tuck your chin into your chest and lift your shoulders off the ground. Twist at the waist, bringing your left elbow to right knee, pushing your left foot away from you. Twist at the waist, bringing your right elbow to left knee, pushing your right foot away from you. Repeat, taking short breaths in and out as you alternate legs.

Standing Crunches

1. Stand with feet at hip width and body weight in your heels. Lift your hands to your head and rest your fingers at your temples.

2. Keeping your chest upright, twist at the waist, bringing your right knee to meet your left elbow. Keep your elbows wide and level with your shoulders. Replace your right foot. Bring your left knee to meet your right elbow. Replace your left foot. Repeat. Take short breaths in and out as you alternate legs.

Hollow Hold

1. Start laying on the floor, facing upwards. Extend your arms overhead until they rest just above the floor. Tuck your chin down to your chest.

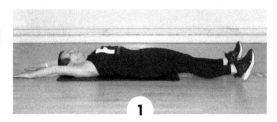

2. Lift your feet off the floor, engaging your core muscles and taking long, slow breaths in and out. Avoid this exercise if you have any lower back issues.

Plank

1. With your feet hip width apart, place your hands on the floor, beneath your shoulders, spreading your fingers.

2. Lower your body until your back is flat and your body weight is evenly distributed between your limbs. Engage your core muscles. Now lower your arms, so that your forearms rest on the floor, with your elbows beneath your shoulders. Take long, slow steady breaths in and out. Aim to increase your plank time as you perform this in your workouts.

Plank Shoulder Tap

1. With your feet hip width apart, place your hands on the floor, beneath your shoulders, spreading your fingers.

2. Lower your body until your back is flat and your body weight is evenly distributed between your limbs. Engage your core muscles. Take steady breaths in and out. Tap your left shoulder with your right hand. Replace your right hand. Tap your right shoulder with your left hand. Replace your left hand. Repeat. Resist moving your hips and keep your back flat.

Plank Jacks

1. With your feet hip width apart, place your hands on the floor, beneath your shoulders, spreading your fingers.

2. Lower your body until your back is flat and your body weight is evenly distributed between your limbs. Engage your core muscles. Take steady breaths in and out. Jump your feet together. Jump your feet back to hip width. Repeat.

Russian Twists

1. Sit on the floor with your heels on the ground and toes upwards, ensuring that your back is straight from your neck to your coccyx. Clasp your hands together and rest them on your stomach.

2. Twisting at the waist and turning your head to the left, reach your clasped hands to your left hip. Twisting your waist in the opposite direction and turning your head, reach your clasped hands to your right hip. Repeat. Take a breath out each time you change direction of movement. To make Russian twists more challenging, bring your heels two inches off the floor, maintaining posture.

Sit Up

1. Laying on the ground, facing upwards, keep your feet together, heels on the ground and toes facing upwards, and rest your fingers at your temples.

2. Keeping your heels on the ground, engage your core muscles, tuck your chin into your chest and sit up. Take a breath in before you sit up and exhale as you sit up. Keeping your chin tucked into your chest, return your fingers to your temples, take a breath in and exhale as you return your back to the floor and your start position.

Toe Touches

1. Start laying on the floor, facing upwards. Bring your knees into your chest and raise your feet above your hips. Place your hands on top of each other and rest them on your thighs.

2. Engage your core muscles, tuck your chin into your chest, take a small breath in and exhale as you lift your shoulders off the floor. Keep your eyes focussed on your feet, to stop your head falling backwards. Keeping your chin tucked into your chest, take a small breath in and exhale as you raise your hands towards your feet. Lower your shoulders three inches approximately. Repeat.

STRETCHES:

During your workout, your muscles will tighten as you put them under stress. To avoid injury and discomfort, always take time to stretch after your workout. Hold these stretches for 20 to 30 seconds each.

Quad Stretch
Standing with your feet hip width apart, bring your right foot to the back of your right thigh, holding just above the ankle with your right hand if possible, for a deeper stretch. Replace your right foot. Bring your left foot to the back of your left thigh, holding just above the ankle if possible with your left hand, for a deeper stretch.

Hamstring Stretch

1. Standing with your feet hip width apart, bring your left foot 12 inches in front of your right foot, approximately. Hinge at the hips, bringing your hips backwards, straightening your left leg and bending your right leg. Rest your hands on your right thigh.

2. Return to standing. Bring your right foot 12 inches in front of your left foot, approximately. Hinge at the hips, bringing your hips backwards, straightening your right leg and bending your left leg. Rest your hands on your left thigh. Return to standing.

Lunge Quad and Glute Stretch

1. Stand with feet shoulder width apart. Put your hands on your hips. Take your left foot a full stride length in front of the right, lowering the right knee just above the ground. Your left heel should be firmly planted on the ground.

2. Push through the left heel to draw your right leg up to a standing position. Repeat with your right leg. Your feet should remain hip distance apart.

Hip Rotation

1. Rotate your hips in big circles in a clockwise direction.

2. After five rotations, change direction and rotate your hips anti-clockwise.

Arm and Shoulder Stretch

1. Standing with your feet hip width apart and shoulders relaxed. Bring your left arm across your chest. For a deeper stretch, hold your left arm with your right hand, above the elbow, and gently ease your left arm further across your chest. Relax both arms.

2. Bring your right arm across your chest. For a deeper stretch, hold your right arm with your left hand, above the elbow, and gently ease your right arm further across your chest. Relax both arms.

Tricep Stretch

1. Standing with your feet hip width apart, reach your left arm overhead. Drop your left hand towards the back of your neck, keeping your elbow close to your head. For a deeper stretch, take your right hand to your left upper arm and gently ease your left arm back further. Relax both arms at your sides. Reach your right arm overhead. Drop your right hand towards the back of your neck, keeping your elbow close to your head.

2. For a deeper stretch, take your left hand to your right upper arm and gently ease your right arm back further. Relax both arms at your sides.

***

Images @alisonvwebster

AMRAPS

Complete AS MANY ROUNDS AS POSSIBLE of these exercises in the allocated time. Each time you repeat the workout, aim to complete more rounds.

AMRAP 10 minutes
10 x forward lunges, alternate legs
10 x reverse lunges, alternate legs
100 x skips
10 x air squats
10 x walk outs
100 x skips

AMRAP 10 minutes
20 second plank
10 x high knees
10 x shoulder press
10 x mountain climbers

AMRAP 10 minutes
10 x press up
10 x high knees
10 x plank jacks
10 x tricep lift

AMRAP 10 minutes
10 x lateral raise
10 x forward lunges
10 x press ups
10 x air squat

AMRAP 20 minutes
12 x burpee
200 metre run
12 x press ups
200 metre run
12 x lateral raise

AMRAP 20 minutes
12 x 10 high knees, 2 reverse lunge
12 x press up
12 x jumping squat
12 x burpee
12 x shoulder press

AMRAP 20 minutes
12 x walk out
12 x press ups
12 x air squat
12 x burpee
400 metre run

AMRAP 20 minutes
12 x forward lunge
12 x shoulder press
12 x burpee
12 x sit up
12 x mountain climbers

AMRAP 30 minutes
15 x forward lunge
15 x plank jacks
15 x burpee
15 x sit up
15 x squat thrust

AMRAP 30 minutes
800 metre run/walk
15 x shoulder press
400 metre run/walk
15 x toe touches
200 metre run/walk
15 x mountain climbers

AMRAP 30 minutes
30 x sit ups
30 x skips
30 second plank
30 x skips
30 x bicycle crunches
30 x skips

AMRAP 30 minutes
100 x high knees
15 x lateral raise
100 x mountain climbers
15 x shoulder press
200 metre run/walk

***

SKIPPING

Skipping works your core, legs and improves stamina.

500 Skips
Every missed skip is a press up. Count these and do all your press ups at the end or do one every time you miss a skip.

Skip Plank Accumulator
100 x skips, 15 second plank
100 x skips, 30 second plank
100 x skips, 45 second plank
100 x skips, 1 minute plank
100 x skips, 1 minute 15 second plank
100 x skips, 1 minute 30 second plank
100 x skips, 1 minute 45 second plank
100x skips, 2 minute plank

AMRAP 20 minutes
Complete as many rounds as possible in 20 minutes of the following:
50 x skips, 5 squat thrusts
50 x skips, 10 shoulder press
50 x skips, 20 press ups

The Exercise Pill

'There is so much evidence to prove that exercise is a pill for so many conditions and a great preventative medicine. Those who exercise will have a 30 per cent less chance of developing a huge range of illnesses, including cardiovascular disease, diabetes, fractures and depression. It needs to be combined with healthy eating for maximum benefit.

'If you have muscular skeletal pain and you don't exercise, the muscles around your joints become weaker. The joints are then unsupported by strong muscle. If there is joint destruction, you need good muscle strength to support those joints. In many cases, you can avoid surgery by increasing muscle density.

'Being sedentary for long periods causes inflammation in the body. By moving, we create an anti inflammatory reaction. This helps with inflammatory and auto immune conditions. It reduces pain in those with osteo or rheumatoid arthritis. As soon as we exercise, our biochemical markers improve. Our blood pressure reduces and our lipid profiles and inflammatory markers improve.

'Exercise releases endorphins, which is hugely useful to those coping with poor mental health. It is effective alongside and often instead of antidepressants and counselling. Those who haven't previously exercised and may be reluctant, enjoy the release of endorphins and seeing their mood improving. Exercising outdoors and reconnecting with nature provides another layer of calm. Exercise is such a great stress buster. I can't imagine my life without it.' –
Manpinder Singh Sahota, GP

***

EMOM

EMOMs are completed every minute on the minute. Complete each round of exercises inside a minute. The remaining time is yours for recovery before the next minute begins. Repeat them at regular intervals to mark your progress.

EMOM 8 minutes

5 x squats
10 x crunches
10 x toe touches

EMOM 8 minutes

20 x mountain climbers
5 x lateral raises
10 x shoulder press

EMOM 8 minutes

Within eight minutes, complete 100 forward lunges. Add two dumbbells held by your sides to add resistance. Every minute on the minute, complete 5 burpees, then continue with forward lunges until you have completed 100 of these.

EMOM 8 minutes

Complete 50 press ups within eight minutes. Every minute on the minute, complete three sit ups, then continue with press ups until you have completed 50 of these.

EMOM 12 minutes

8 x high knees
8 x squats
8 x shoulder press

EMOM 12 minutes

8 x squat thrusts
8 x plank shoulder touches
8 x mountain climbers

EMOM 12 minutes

10 x mountain climbers
10 x lateral raise
10 x tricep extension

EMOM 12

Complete 500 mountain climbers within 12 minutes. Every minute on the minute, complete a 20 second plank, then continue with mountain climbers until you have completed 500 of these.

EMOM 15 minutes

5 x burpees
5 x squats
5 x jumping squats

EMOM 15

10 x lateral raises
10 x squats
20 x skips

EMOM 15

Complete 100 burpees within 15 minutes. Every minute on the minute, complete 20 skips, then continue with burpees until you have completed 100 of these.

EMOM 15

10 second plank
10 x squat thrusts
10 x sit ups

***

Ladders

Repeat each exercise with the highest number of repetitions first, then repeat them with the next number of reps, until you work your way down to the lowest number of reps. If you want to make your workout more mentally challenging, start with the lowest number first. If you want a longer workout, when you finish your ladder, repeat it in the opposite direction. So, if you finished on the least reps, work your way back up to the highest number of reps.

30 25 20 15 10 5
second hollow hold
sit up
second plank

30 25 20 15 10 5
bicycle crunches
plank shoulder taps
sit ups

30 25 20 15 10 5
mountain climbers
shoulder press
air squats

30 25 20 15 10 5
toe touches
lateral raise
jumping squats

30 25 20 15 10 5
bicycle crunches
press ups
shoulder press

30 25 20 15 10 5
second plank
walk outs
tricep extension

30 25 20 15 10 5
jumping squats with 180 degree jump
shoulder press
bicycle crunches

18 15 12 9 6 3
squat thrust
press up
mountain climbers
crunches

18 15 12 9 6 3
jumping squats
walk outs
second plank
plank jacks

18 15 12 9 6 3
hollow hold
sit up
Russian twists
bicycle crunches

18 15 12 9 6 3
plank shoulder taps
second plank
plank jacks
second plank
crunches

18 15 12 9 6 3
mountain climbers
air squat
jumping squats
reverse lunges

18 15 12 9 6 3
lateral raise
tricep extension
press up
squat thrust

18 15 12 9 6 3
burpee
high knees
mountain climbers
walk out

***

Burpee to Failure

Burpees are a fantastic whole body exercise.
Set a timer for 30 seconds. In the first 30 seconds, complete two burpees. In the second 30 seconds, add two burpees to complete four reps. Every 30 seconds, add two more burpees until you can't complete any more inside 30 seconds.
If you are unable to perform chest to floor burpees safely, choose half burpees.
Choose stepping burpees, rather than jumping, if this works better for you.
If you want to make this harder, extend the time to 45 seconds or one minute.
Each time you repeat the workout, aim to increase your reps.

***

THE 550

The 550 is a ladder of 550 reps, gradually decreasing in number. Swap the exercises to suit you. Each time you repeat the ladder, measure your time and try to shave some seconds off. If you want to make it more challenging mentally, start with the lowest number of reps and work up to the highest number. If you want to improve your stamina further, repeat the 550 ladder.

550 Whole Body Example:

100 mountain climbers

90 air squats

80 toe touches

70 second plank

60 squat thrusts

50 shoulder press

40 sit ups

30 walk outs

20 lateral raises

10 burpees

550 Core Example:

100 toe touches

90 bicycle crunches

80 Russian twists

70 plank shoulder taps

60 second plank

50 sit ups

40 plank jacks

30 second hollow hold

20 crunches

10 second plank

***

Deck of Cards

This is one of my favourite portable workouts and I use it a lot when I'm travelling. Use a regular pack of playing cards. Give each suit: diamonds, spades, hearts and clubs, a value. If diamonds is squats and you turn over the 5 of diamonds, do 5 squats. Ace is 1, picture cards are 10. Joker varies according to what you are trying to achieve but should represent a challenge. Continue turning over cards, each representing an exercise, until you have completed the pack.

Deck of Cards Example:

Diamonds – burpees

Spades – skips

Hearts – sit ups

Clubs – air squats

Joker – 400 metre run

***

Stretch

In the same way that you warm up and mobilise each of your muscles in turn, do the same when you stretch. Hold each stretch for 20 seconds and repeat if you feel you need to.

Start with a quad stretch, then ham strings and a lunge, on both legs. Rotate your hips. Bring your arms across your chest and behind your shoulder, to stretch your arms, shoulders and triceps. Roll your shoulders and stand tall, with shoulders back and down.

***

I Did It My Way

'Before a 30 mile speed march over Dartmoor as a Royal Marine Commando, I was given this advice, 'Everything has to end at some point. Don't let yourself down. Don't let your Brothers down. Dig deep. Stand strong. And finish as a fine body of men.' –
James Haward

'I wasn't sure about exercise. I was tripping and falling too often, which scared me. However, encouraged by a friend, I started working with a personal trainer. The change in my mobility and strength within a few short months was amazing and I now have so much more stamina. After strengthening my muscles, I no longer need surgery to my right knee. Best of all, aged 75, I now feel empowered, rather than lost and abandoned.' –
Gillian Williams

FEED YOUR ENGINE

IF we don't get our nutrition right, no amount of exercise will create optimum health. What we eat and drink affects us not just physically, but mentally. It impacts our mood, our focus, our decision making and therefore, those around us, too. Ask yourself this: what car do you drive? If it's powered by petrol, what happens if you put diesel in the engine? It won't work. What if you put no fuel in the engine? Would you expect to be able to keep on driving? Of course not. How about if you put too much fuel in and flood your engine? It won't move, right? These days, our cars probably last 10 years, if we're lucky, if we treat them well, give them the right fuel and service them regularly. Our bodies may last eight or nine times as long, maybe longer. Surely they deserve at least as much respect, in order for us to have a healthy, vital, energetic life. Put the right fuel in your body for the performance you are expecting. Our bodies are an amazing set of biomechanics and super smart. If we invest in our bodies, they will reward us. If we treat them badly, they will let us know. There are a few rules I live by and instil in my clients:

Eat what you need, not what you want. Think of food as fuel to make your engine work efficiently.

The 80/20 rule. Eat clean 80 per cent of the time. This means prepare meals from scratch, using raw ingredients, avoiding processed food and drinks, which are riddled with salt and sugar. Indulge in your favourite treats 20 per cent of the time; alcohol, crisps, cake etc and that 20 per cent will not impact your health. Enjoy every mouthful without guilt. Food is to be enjoyed. It is not your enemy. This is key to maintaining a healthy relationship with food and drink.

Eat carbohydrates on high energy days only. These are our energy building blocks, so use them wisely. Only put in as much energy as your engine will use.

Eat more fruit and vegetables. Tight budget? Go to a market stall or supermarket at the end of the day when they are reduced price or if you have space and time, grow your own. Your body will thank you for the vitamins and minerals. Your metabolism will thank you if you eat less meat. Vegetables grown above the ground contain little or no starch. Eat lots of these. Vegetables grown below the ground contain more starch. Eat less of these.

Drink eight large tumblers of water a day to remain hydrated. This is vital in order for your cells and organs to function efficiently.

Drink less booze if you know you drink too much. Stop pouring sugar down your neck. Seek help if you know you need to.

Never forget breakfast. Your body will go into starvation mode and store the food you ate last as fat, to preserve your organ, muscle and bone function.

Eat every three to four hours to maintain a steady metabolism, even mood, energy levels and good sleep.

***

Nutritionist Fred Wadsworth, MRCOG FRCS Ed NTCC, Clinical Director of CorPerformance, specialising in human performance, agrees. His clients include international athletes in football, rugby and cricket. He says, 'I believe in eating for purpose and direction. So you need to work out what your goal is for your body and you can then eat to support whatever that goal may be. That will vary enormously from someone trying to lose weight to a professional athlete. Whatever your goal, it's essential to take notice of the microbiome and how you eat for health there, as that will reflect in your wellness. The microbiome is a collection of bacteria that lives on your body and the more bacteria that is in a healthy balance in your body, the healthier you are. It affects everything from your chances of having a heart attack to having depression. It's important that we eat in a way to support all these different bacteria. So in your fruit and vegetables you will have a blueberry bug and a cabbage bug and an apple bug. You don't want lots of just one, you need a bit of all of them. Variety in diet is a powerful thing with powerful consequences. The chances of you being obese if you are born abdominally are 30 per cent higher than if you are born vaginally. That is directly linked to the first bacteria that grows on your body. We have been obsessed with single fault – focussing on a high fat diet or high salt or high sugar diet. The truth it is more complex. The less of these we eat the better, but there is no one single culprit.'

He adds. 'Most people have 10 recipes and this food will always be in their household. For those seeking weight loss, there are a lot of food plans available but these fail because someone else's monotony gets boring and can't be maintained. Instead, if you have a decent amount of protein, wholegrains, a variety of fruit and vegetables and an appropriate relationship with alcohol, you can take your ingredients anywhere your palate takes you.'

***

Metabolism

If we stabilise our metabolism, we have energy to carry us through our day and restful sleep. Our metabolism – created by the chemical reactions in our body involved in maintaining the state of our cell function – doesn't just affect our body's strength and stamina. It's also vital for a healthy mind, affecting our mood and decision making. These chemical processes require energy. Our BMR (basal metabolic rate), the rate at which our bodies use energy, is affected by our body size, age, gender and genes. As we age, we lose muscle mass and gain fat, meaning we burn energy at a slower rate. Lean muscle tissue requires more energy than fat cells, creating a higher BMR. Men have more muscle mass, heavier bones and less body fat, which is why they require a slightly higher calorie intake. Our genes also partly define our muscle size, affecting our metabolism.

Therefore, as we age, getting our nutrition working for us becomes even more important. Fred explains, 'From our mid-20s we lose about 10 per cent of our muscle mass per annum unless we do something to stop that. The muscle mass burns the energy and drives our metabolic rate. There will be a fall in energy through life.

'Additionally, the adrenapause in men and menopause in women, where you have a fundamental change in hormonal function may have some impact on our metabolic rate and how we manage energy supplies, alongside the aches and pains of age, which will tend to drive activity levels down. It's a gradual slope rather than any sudden changes with each passing decade. We accrue more injuries and have more activities we feel unable to do. However, the biomechanical distress caused by long periods of sitting is also damaging. After decades of sitting, particularly in cars and at desks, we end up with disruption in how our lower limbs work. It causes short hamstrings, short quads and issues with our glutes. Then when we try and run in later life, we end up in pain. So we become less biomechanically able to exercise and that drives down our energy requirements. Even if you have exercised all your life it will become harder age 50 onwards. There will have been micro tears in your tissue. Changes in thyroid as we age will affect metabolic rate and energy levels, too.'

***

But we can adjust all of these factors with appropriate exercise and sound nutrition. A great way to achieve a steady metabolism is to ensure that our diet includes foods with slow release energy, low glycaemic index (low GI) foods. These burn more slowly than high GI foods, which release energy quickly, so that we hit an insulin spike, then our energy levels quickly drop. Low GI foods maintain our metabolism by regulating blood sugar, leaving us feeling satiated for longer and preventing tiredness. In doing so, they also help reduce cholesterol and lower the risk of heart disease.

Foods which are high in fibre fall into this category. They include fruit and vegetables such as apples, pears, kiwi fruit, cherries, grapes, oranges, peas, carrots, cauliflower, broccoli and red peppers. The more colour we have on our plate, the better mix of vitamins and minerals we add to our diet. Choose sweet potatoes, which metabolise more slowly in our body, instead of white potatoes.

Avoid high GI processed white bread, flour, pastry, rice and pasta. These have had the fibre content stripped away. Instead, choose wholegrain varieties of these foods, oat bran, rolled oats, wholegrain cereals, quinoa, cous cous and pearl barley.

Further sources of low GI foods are beans and pulses, including kidney beans, butter beans, chickpeas and lentils, which will also boost our protein, zinc and iron levels.

***

Mood Food

The brain cannot work without energy. The ability to concentrate and focus comes from an adequate, steady supply of energy, in the form of glucose in our blood, which feeds our brain. To release a steady flow of energy, keeping us mentally alert throughout the day, choose unprocessed low GI foods, instead of their processed equivalent.

Essential fatty acids are excellent for brain function. The most effective Omega 3s occur naturally in oily fish, like salmon, herring, mackerel, sardines, pilchards and kippers. There are great plant sources too, including flaxseed, soya beans, pumpkin seeds and walnuts. Omega 3s have been linked to an improvement in memory and help us manage mood by releasing serotonin in the brain.

Vitamin C rich foods, including berries, blackcurrants, citrus fruits and broccoli, further contribute towards an increase in mental agility. Broccoli also contains vitamin K, which assists our cognitive skills and helps regulate our nervous system.

Adding pumpkin seeds to your diet, either as a snack, or added to cereal, yogurt, smoothies and stir fries, will also enhance memory and cognitive skills. These little seeds are also full of stress busting magnesium.

Fred adds, 'If you look after your microbiome by having a healthy, balanced diet, then you will be looking after your mood. This means definitely maintaining a blood sugar balance and there is good evidence that Omega 3s decrease depression. Highly processed foods are not helpful here.'

***

Sleep

Many protein rich foods, including poultry and eggs and other food sources, including milk, oats, bananas, eggs and peanuts, contain the amino acid tryptophan that causes sleepiness. Carbohydrates make tryptophan available to the brain, which is why we feel drowsy after eating a carbohydrate-heavy meal. Tryptophan is converted first into serotonin, then to melatonin in the brain, secreted in the pineal gland and it's this process that induces and maintains sleep.

Some of us feel a temporary lull in alertness in the afternoon. This is linked to our circadian rhythm, within which we feel naturally tired at two times, 2am and 2pm.

***

Fred explains, 'You give your body a biochemical job to metabolise food, postprandial thermogenesis. Protein causes the highest thermogenesis, so high protein meals within an hour of sleep may make it harder to sleep. To get from consciousness to restful sleep you need to drop your core temperature by half a degree. If you go to the gym just before you go to bed, it's harder to get to sleep. It's the same if you go to bed in a hot room. You are too hot to be able to drop that temperature. Our insulin resistance increases at the end of the day, so it's a poor time to have carbohydrate loads because we are least physiologically able to digest and process them. Ideally, we don't want to eat within a couple of hours of sleep. If you are going to have a carbohydrate-heavy meal, the further back it is from sleep the better.'

***

Start the Day Right

I have a few rules with my clients and not missing breakfast is high on the list. Many start by telling me that they don't like eating early in the day, that it makes them feel sick or that their stomach and taste buds aren't ready to accept food before 11am. Without exception, even those who have held this habit for most of their lives, gradually turn it around by starting with small amounts of food, maybe half a banana, and increasing to an acceptable sustainable breakfast pattern from there. For most people, their mental clarity and energy output is greatly improved by hydrating and eating within an hour of waking and their metabolism becomes far more effective.

'For the majority of people, breakfast is really important,' says Fred, 'so that they don't reach for that muffin at 11am. For most of us, our circadian rhythm leaves us a little insulin resistant, so to have sugar first thing is not clever. To have a poached egg on wholegrain toast is very clever. Wholegrain and protein is a great start to the day. A well-structured, low GI breakfast is a good idea. That way, your appetite will not reappear until lunch. Then you are not likely to overeat at lunch. Suddenly the tide is flowing with you rather than against you. If you follow breakfast by having a salad lunch and fish with green beans and broccoli for dinner, you are on the right track.'

***

TRY THESE BREAKFAST RECIPES

Overnight Oats

This is a cool, slow release energy summer breakfast or heat it up for a warming start to the day when it's colder.

Take a dessert bowl and fill it two thirds with porridge oats. Top with one tsp each of ground flaxseed, chia seeds, cinnamon and one tbsp each of your favourite dried fruit. I use raisins and cranberries. Pour a third of a pint of almond milk over and stir. Cover and refrigerate overnight. In the morning, add one third to a bowl. Heat in the microwave for one minute if preferred.

Top with more fresh fruit and a handful of nuts of your choice and pumpkin seeds.

Protein Pancakes

Mash one banana. Add two whisked eggs and one tsp of cinnamon. Heat a non-stick frying pan to a medium setting. Add one heaped tablespoon of the banana batter to the pan.

Turn when the underside is golden brown. When both sides are golden brown they are ready. Top with Greek yogurt, blueberries, a drizzle of honey or maple syrup and chia seeds.

***

Hydration

Every cell and organ in our body needs water to function. We should aim to drink eight glasses of it a day. Water makes up two thirds of our body weight and we lose it throughout the day, due to the normal actions of our bodies: sweating, breathing and passing urine.

If you are experiencing dry eyes or a dry mouth, headache, muscle cramp, fatigue, dark urine or dizziness and have no existing medical conditions, there is a strong likelihood that you are dehydrated.

Caffeinated drinks and alcohol dehydrate the body by decreasing our production of the anti-diuretic hormone, stored in the pituitary gland.

What if you don't like water? Fix it with one of these alternatives. Try fruit tea, water with a slice of fruit added or vegetable juice. Foods with a high water content will also contribute to your hydration, eg oranges, watermelon, tomatoes and cucumber.

The first thing I insist my clients do is drink warm water and a squeeze of lemon juice, first thing each morning. Some now call it their lemon tea. This is a rich source of nutrients, including calcium, potassium and vitamin C. Lemon helps maintain our immune system. It's also a blood purifier and an antiseptic.

'Thirst is like many biological triggers. It works on feedback,' explains Fred. 'If you stop drinking, you feel thirsty. If you ignore that for long enough, you stop noticing you are thirsty. A lot of people don't think they are thirsty and drink no more than a cup of tea a day. Our biological feedback here is the colour of our urine. It should be colourless and you should drink whatever amount of water you need to in order to make this happen and this will vary from person to person, according to physical size and exercise level. The common mistake people make is to under hydrate. Most people don't drink enough, don't look at their urine and wonder why they end up with a renal stent. If you stop drinking altogether, your body is likely to survive for just a matter of days.

'If you are a sprinter or high jumper you may have dips in hydration to save a kilogram or two to achieve your goal. If you are about to run a marathon, you don't want to start any drier than you possibly need to. In competitive sport, it's vital to get the physiological balance right and to balance your hydration accordingly.'

***

TEN HEALTH BENEFITS OF DRINKING WARM WATER AND LEMON

1. Lemon is an excellent and rich source of vitamin C, an essential nutrient that protects the body against immune system deficiencies.
2. Lemons contain pectin, which is very beneficial for colon health as it serves as a powerful antibacterial device. Drinking warm water and lemon first thing each day will help flush out toxins.
3. It aids digestion and encourages the production of bile.
4. It's a great source of citric acid, potassium, calcium, phosphorus and magnesium.
5. It helps prevent the growth and multiplication of bacteria that causes infection and disease.
6. It helps reduce pain and inflammation of the joints, as it dissolves uric acid.
7. The potassium content of lemons helps nourish brain and nerve cells.
8. It strengthens the liver by providing energy to the liver enzymes when they are too dilute. It helps balance the calcium and oxygen levels in the liver, too.
9. It is of immense benefit to skin, helping prevent the formation of acne and wrinkles.
10. Lemon juice helps replenish body salts, especially useful after a strenuous exercise session.

***

Snacking

In order to regulate our metabolism, we should be eating something every three to four hours. So snacking plays an important role when it is mindful and used in this way. Ideally, we should have a small, nutritious snack between each of our main three meals, breakfast, lunch and dinner. Snacking only becomes an issue when it isn't mindful and is done for other reasons. Next time you are reaching for the biscuit tin, ask yourself: am I hungry or am I bored, tired or stressed?

Don't mistake hunger for thirst. Have a glass of water and ask yourself whether you are still hungry for that snack. The best way to avoid snacks with poor nutritional value is to not buy them in the first place! As soon as they are in your cupboard, they will tempt you.

Choose snacks with a high fibre content, some protein, vitamins and minerals. An apple and a small block of cheese, crackers and houmous, a handful of unsalted nuts, fruit and vegetable sticks are all great choices.

***

Food Groups

Understanding each of the food groups helps us make informed choices and create a balanced, colourful, tempting, sustainable, nutritious diet. Fred explains further below:

MACRONUTRIENTS

Carbohydrates

'Our carbs should relate to our energy balance. If we are the weight and body fat that we want to be, then we can eat the carbs at the rate we do now. If we want to gain weight, we probably need to eat more and if we want to lose weight, we should eat less.

'Fibrous carbohydrates come from all the stuff that grows above the ground and we ought to eat these in large volumes in great variety on a daily basis.

'White carbs are a form of processed carbohydrate, which is the big demon in our modern diet. That food has been through a lot of machinery and a lot of the digestive work has already been done, so we absorb the energy in that food too quickly for our evolutionary biology. As our body is unable to cope with the big influx of carbohydrate energy, it will create poor glucose control and fat deposition. A whole bunch of stuff starts to go wrong because too much energy is arriving too quickly.

'Wholegrain carbs are a better option for our bodies. The fibre content of wholegrain carbs slows the gut absorption speed and we are able to cope with that physiologically much better.'

***

Protein

'Protein in our diet controls our appetite and this is particularly the case in the Western world. We live in an environment with too much processed, high sugar, low quality food available and it tastes nice. Your best way of controlling those cravings is to not be hungry and protein is the biggest bullet to do that. Improve the protein content of our diet and that alone has been proven to aid weight loss, as it affects calorie consumption. In adults, it counters the loss of muscle mass. If we lose muscle mass, we reduce our basal metabolic rate and therefore require less calories. But if we are not aware of this, we consume more calories than we biologically need and lay down fat. Along the way, we start to damage our insulin sensitivity and insulin resistance – the need of the body to produce high levels of insulin to control blood sugar. This increases the risk of diabetes, dementia and cancer. Looking after our protein intake is key to good health for all these reasons. It controls our muscle mass, so we burn more energy and are less hungry, so we eat less rubbish.'

***

TRY THIS PUNCHY PROTEIN AND VITAMIN RICH BRUNCH, LUNCH OR SUPPER

Tortilla

Line a pie dish with a non-stick baking sheet.

Take your favourite vegetables. Leftovers will do.

I like using half a roasted red pepper, sliced and a fist full of spinach leaves, quickly stir fried in a non-stick pan. Add these to the dish.

Next, whisk six eggs with a fork. Add seasoning and two tsp of your favourite herbs. I like fresh oregano and basil but dried herbs will do. Add two large tbsp of natural yogurt and mix. Add the egg mixture to the dish. Place on the oven and cook on Gas 6 / 200 degrees C for 30 minutes. It's cooked when a skewer comes out clean.

Cut in half to serve two for lunch or supper. Or cut into six, freeze the portions and pop them into your lunch box as required.

***

Fats

'Fat consumption ought to be governed by our calorie balance. If we are overweight, we need to be careful about our fat consumption. An amateur tri-athlete who wants to eat some fat should go ahead because they are burning high amounts of calories.

'For most of us however, the fewer saturated fats we consume, the better. Keep them to a minimum. These are all the animal fats. Coconut oil, which has been super fashionable, should also be included here. It's no better than other saturated fats so we should be consuming minimal amounts of it.

'The fats we should be avoiding altogether are polyunsaturates, which have been highly processed. It's far better to have a small amount of pure butter than to have margarine or corn oil in our diet, for this reason. Further, when we heat these they do nasty things chemically and generate transfats, and these are really bad for us, increasing our cholesterol.

'Heating fats is a big issue for our health and we need to get it right. There is no reason for smoking oil in a pan. To make a sauce, put the onions and oil in together and add oil to the meat or fish rather than oil the pan. If we are cooking steak, stand it on its fatty rim and use that to oil the pan. It is saturated fat but it cannot undergo harmful changes as it heats. A little butter used in this way is fine, as is a little olive oil.'

***

MICRONUTRIENTS - VITAMINS AND MINERALS

Macronutrients are supported by micronutrients – vitamins and minerals. Getting the right blend of both means our bodies are energised and able to repair and renew healthy cells, supporting our organs, bones and muscles.

Vitamin A
What does it do?
Tough talking vitamin A powers our immune system against infection, increases our vision in dim light and keeps skin and body tissue healthy.

Where can I find it?

Find vitamin A in cheese, eggs, oily fish, liver, milk and yogurt. We can contribute to our vitamin A intake by including good sources of beta-carotene, found in red, yellow, leafy green vegetables, sweet potatoes and yellow fruit including mangos, apricots and papayas in our diet, as beta carotene can be converted into vitamin A by the body.

How much is enough?
0.7mg daily for men and 0.6mg daily for women is adequate. Like vitamin E, any vitamin A not immediately used by our bodies is stored for future use.

Vitamin B6
What does it do?
This allows the body to use and store energy from protein and carbohydrates in food, contributing to a healthy metabolism. It also helps to form haemoglobin, the substance in red blood cells that carries oxygen around the body and helps control our hormones and skin health.

Where can I find it?
Great sources of vitamin B6 include pork, poultry, fish, wholegrain bread and rice, wheatgerm, oatmeal, eggs, soya beans, peanuts milk and potatoes.

How much is enough?
1.4mg per day for men and 1.2mg per day for women is recommended.

Vitamin C
What does it do?
Also known as ascorbic acid, vitamin C functions include maintenance of cells and connective tissue, which give support to other tissue and organs and helps the healing of wounds. It's vital for preventing eye disease, supporting our immune system, renewing and repairing tissue and iron absorption.

Where can I find it?
Find vitamin C in a wide variety of fruit and vegetables, including red and green

peppers, strawberries, blackcurrants, raspberries, blueberries, broccoli and sprouts, kiwi fruit, leafy greens, guava, citrus fruits, tomatoes and peas.

How much is enough?

Adults need 40mg of vitamin C each day. It is not stored in the body for protracted periods of time, so we need to have it in our diet every day.

Vitamin D

What does it do?

Vitamin D helps to absorb minerals and protect our bones by regulating the amount of calcium and phosphate in the body. These nutrients are needed to keep bones, teeth and muscles healthy. A lack of vitamin D can lead to bone pain and tenderness.

Where can I find it?

From spring to autumn, most of us should be able to get vitamin D from sunlight on our skin. It's produced by our body under the skin as a reaction to sunlight. However, when exposing the skin to sun, take care to protect it with sun screen. During autumn and winter, when we are exposed to less sunlight, our vitamin D intake will be less, though it can be found in small quantities in oily fish, red meat, liver and egg yolks.

How much is enough?

It's worth considering a supplement to diet here, particularly in the darker months. Fred adds, 'This is top of the list of supplements. There is lots of deficiency. There is a huge weight of science behind this. We would be foolhardy to not make sure our vitamin D intake is sufficient. Most people can take 1000 units (IU) up to 60 kilos in weight, 2000 units (IU) up to 110 kilos.'

Vitamin E

What does it do?

Vitamin E's functions include acting as an antioxidant, protecting body tissue from damage from free radicals (atoms with a missing electron, that weaken cells) and strengthening cell membranes. It also assists the formation of red blood cells and helps widen blood vessels, to prevent blood from clotting within them. This helps maintain healthy skin, eyes and strengthens the immune system against viruses and bacteria.

Where can I find it?
Vitamin E is in a wide variety of foods, though it is most heavily concentrated in plant oils, such as olive oil. It's also contained in nuts, seeds, wheatgerm, soya beans and leafy green vegetables.

How much is enough?
We should be able to get all the vitamin E we need from our diet. 4mg for men and 3mg for women daily is recommended. Any vitamin E our body doesn't need immediately is cleverly stored for future use.

***

FRED'S FIVE REASONS TO EAT FRUIT AND VEGETABLES

These are the best source of the best kind of nutrients in our diet.

There are polyphenols and antioxidants here that we can't get from any other source.

We need potassium from fruit and vegetables, which is our body's antidote to sodium.

Every piece we eat reduces our chances of dying by five per cent. That's a pretty big thing from a single food channel.

If there is one single action to do for our diet to live healthier and longer it is to eat more fruit and vegetables.

FRUIT SALAD

Keep a chopped fruit salad in the fridge to snack on. Choose all your favourites, the brighter the better, to get a good range of vitamins and minerals. Squeeze lemon or lime on cut apple to prevent it discolouring.

***

Calcium
What does it do?
Calcium is crucial for cell renewal in healthy bones and tissue.

Fred adds, 'In order to absorb calcium, we must have sufficient vitamin D. The primary role of vitamin D is to allow us to absorb calcium in our bones. If we add calcium but don't top up our vitamin D, we might as well not bother. Animal dairy products and calcium rich plants are important for our diets as these are the most easily absorbed into the body. These are the most available and whole food sources. If not bovine dairy, go for sheep or goat varieties, which are both widely available. These come with a calorie intake however, so large amounts of milk and cheese are not advisable. But if we are having a big variety of fruit and vegetables each day, we will absorb a decent amount of calcium.'

Where can I find it?
Find calcium in dark leafy greens, milk, cheese, fish and almonds.

How much is enough?
700mg per day is recommended for adults.

Folate
What does it do?
Also known as vitamin B9, folate helps the body form healthy red blood cells. The manmade form of folate is called folic acid.

Where can I find it?
Find folate in liver, lentils, beans, asparagus, avocado, spinach, broccoli and other leafy green vegetables.

How much is enough?
200 micrograms per day is adequate for adults.

Iron
What does it do?
Iron helps make red blood cells, which carry oxygen around the body and improve muscle and bone function and repair. A lack of iron can lead to anaemia.

Where can I find it?
Good sources of iron include liver, red meat, beans, nuts, dried apricots, wholegrains and dark green leafy vegetables such as kale and watercress.

How much is enough?
Aim for 8.7mg each day for men and 14.8mg for women. This drops to 8.7mg a day for women over age 50. This can be sourced from our daily diet without the need for supplements.

Magnesium
What does it do?
Magnesium helps turn the food we eat into energy. The process is called glycosis, where stored glucose is converted into energy for our body. It also helps to make sure that the parathyroid glands, which produce hormones that are important for bone health, work normally and assists muscle and nerve function.

Where can I find it?
Find magnesium in leafy green vegetables, nuts, wholegrain rice, wholegrain bread, fish, meat and dairy foods.

How much is enough?
Adult men require 300mg per day, women need 270mg per day. We should be able to get all the magnesium we need from our daily diet.

Manganese
What does it do?
Manganese helps create and activate the enzymes in the body. Enzymes are proteins that help the body carry out chemical reactions, including breaking down food.

Where can I find it?
Wholegrain bread, nuts, wholegrain cereals and green vegetables all contain manganese.

How much is enough?
All the manganese we need should be available in our daily diet.

Omega 3
What does it do?
Omega 3 fatty acids are a group of punchy polyunsaturated fats found in a wide variety of foods and an essential part of our diet. They help prevent heart disease, lowering blood pressure and reducing a build up of fat in our arteries, are anti-inflammatory, they regulate our nervous system, improve memory, reasoning, cognitive skills and help prevent age related vision loss and arthritis. They also help reduce cholesterol and prevent hypertension.

Where can I find Omega 3s?
Find Omega 3s in oily fish, including sardines, mackerel, herring and salmon.

However, avoid eating oily fish more than twice a week, due to the risk of absorbing marine pollution. Other sources include cod, prawns, flaxseed, walnuts, cauliflower, tofu, spinach and kale.

How much is enough?
Fred says, 'This is a no brainer supplement. Less than one per cent of people have a reasonable level. They are very important. We just want Omega 3 – we don't need Omega 6 and 9 supplements. 1g a day for women and 1.5g per day for men is enough. A tin of sardines contains 1.8g of the vital EPA and DHA elements of Omega 3.'

Potassium
What does it do?
Potassium is a vital mineral for cell function, controlling the balance of fluids in the body. It assists heart function (potassium helps muscles contract), controls kidney function and maintains healthy blood pressure.

Where can I find it?
Good sources include white beans, spinach, potatoes, apricots, squash, yogurt, salmon, avocados, mushrooms, parsnips, pulses, shellfish, turkey, chicken and bananas.

How much is enough?
Adults need 3,500mg per day. We should be able to get all the potassium we need from our diet.

Phosphorus
What does it do?
Phosphorus is big contributor to metabolism and cell repair, helping build strong bones and teeth.

Where can I find it?
Sources include pumpkin seeds, cheese, fish, shellfish, Brazil nuts, lentils and tofu.

How much is enough?
550mg per day is enough for men and women. We should be able to get all the phosphorus we need from our diet.

Selenium
What does it do?
Selenium packs a big antioxidant punch, protecting our cells from damage and creating cell renewal and good cognitive function.

Where can I find it?
We can find selenium in Brazil nuts, fish, turkey, chicken, beef and wholegrains.

How much is enough?
75 micrograms a day for men and 60 micrograms a day for women. If we eat nuts, meat and fish, we should be able to get all the selenium we need from our daily diet.

***

Gut Health

Maintaining good gut health refers directly to Fred's observations on the importance of balancing the microbiome. There is a fast expanding wealth of science pointing to the huge impact on our bodies from poor gut health. However, there are steps we can take to assist us here, including a regular intake of probiotics and prebiotics.

Fred explains, 'Probiotics – these are the bugs I mentioned earlier, that are helpful in supporting a good gut bacteria balance, particularly if we have been unwell with diarrhea or irritable bowel syndrome or are requiring antibiotics. A probiotic can be a really helpful supplement here.

'Prebiotics – this means taking the foods that support the right balance in our gut. If we are eating six or seven fruit and vegetables a day, have a high fibre intake and eat some natural yogurt, we will be going a long way to taking care of our gut bacteria. If we balance our microbiome in this way, it can be transformational for our health.'

Fasting

There is a lot of evidence pointing to fasting as being useful for detoxing and keeping our weight gain under control. However, it isn't a quick weight loss fix and shouldn't ever be regarded as such.

Fred explains, 'I think it's very difficult to get fasting right unless we are already on a tidy diet. I don't like my clients to do it until they have had eight to 12 weeks of very well established correct eating. We don't want to have big fat weekends followed by fasting to catch up. Instead, we need to be rigid and effective about it. A 5:2 diet should allow some steady weight loss. A woman should look to consuming no more than 500 calories and 600 for a man on the two days, which do not need to be consecutive. I'd recommend maybe a protein pot of eggs and spinach, with salad leaves, a box of sugar snap peas, some grapes and blueberries. Protein and fibre are the places we need to go for those calories. We need to see the food that we eat on our fasting days as appetite control, nothing else and we need to eat it at regular intervals during the day so we avoid going to bed hungry. If we pick our two busiest days in the week, we can just quietly get on with it and barely notice and it won't disturb social plans than might revolve around eating.'

***

Fasted Cardio

If we are already on a balanced, nutritionally rich diet and prefer to exercise first thing in the morning, before breakfast, this is possible due to the fat stores we have built up from the previous day. I prefer my early morning clients to exercise after a light healthy snack, maybe a banana and a glass of milk and enjoy a nutrient dense breakfast afterwards. Those extra calories fight fatigue and offer the best possible use of time and energy.

Fred adds, 'If you are a serious amateur athlete, you can drive your body to increase its fat burning threshold by using low intensity cardio in a low glycogen environment. Low intensity cardio when you are fasting is fine. The higher the intensity, you stop burning fat and start burning glycogen and that can cause low blood sugar and make us feel light headed. Other than that, our physiology will look after us. It's acceptable training stress to put on the body for short periods. If we are going to train early on a fasting day, that's the best time. If we are going to train later on a fasting day, high intensity training may be harder to fuel and it will feel psychologically harder as our body resists.'

***

Alcohol

I encourage new clients to complete a food diary, to monitor their food groups and calorie intake. It's a useful tool if we find our nutrition is slipping, as it forces us to be more mindful of this. However, it can sometimes reveal that although our food intake is well balanced, what we drink may well not be and that there are hidden sugary calories here. In some cases, I have encouraged clients to keep an alcohol diary, too. If we fall into the trap of only drinking at the weekend, for instance, but the weekend starts on Friday night and ends on Sunday and we aren't considering how many units we are drinking in this time, we can quickly discover that we have drunk more calories over almost half the week than we have eaten and the balance needs to be rectified here, both in terms of weight gain and the stress on our organs. If reducing alcohol consumption becomes difficult or stressful, please consider seeking a counsellor to help with this.

Fred explains, 'Alcohol is a suppressant of neural activity so in a convoluted way, alcohol is a downer even though it appears to elevate our mood. It brings the teenager out in us, which inhibits our decision making and therefore we are less strategic in our decisions, so that a lamp post becomes incredibly attractive to climb up, in a way that it wouldn't if we hadn't had alcohol. Our excitement fires furiously, burning up lots of neurotransmitters in the brain and the next day we feel awful because we have to pay back the fun tax.

'We sleep because alcohol sends us into a recovery phase but that recovery can't happen until the alcohol is eliminated from our bodies. If we had half a bottle of wine before we went to bed, it might not be fully metabolised in our body until 3am, and only then can we start deep sleep. Our alarm then goes off at 7am and we wonder why we feel half dead. We may have enjoyed the night before but it will leave us with an emotional overdraft and that's why it can leave us with negative and depressive feelings.

'Incidentally, the idea of having a glass of red wine a day for improved health is total myth and nonsense. There is a linear relationship between our alcohol consumption and our mortality. People make their own choices but there is no argument for the consumption of alcohol as a healthy substance. If we want the health benefits of red wine, we are far better off having a handful of blueberries.'

***

Sugar

Too much sugar too often stresses the organs that control our metabolism, wrecking any good intentions we had about our diet. It prevents the pancreas, which creates insulin, to function properly. It affects our mood, causing lethargy, irritation and tiredness.

'If you eat lots of sugar, you stop tasting the sugar,' says Fred. 'The general rule is the less the better. However, a little is ok. If we add a little brown sugar to our porridge, our body is not going to notice. All the fibre and healthy starch in the porridge is not going to register a small hit of sugar. But if we sit down with a packet of Haribo, we will be pulling our evolutionary tail.

'If we give a person a raspberry they think it tastes lovely. Then give them a block of fudge and the fudge tastes lovely. Then the next raspberry after the fudge tastes horrible. In doing that, we have bludgeoned our sense of sweet. If we reconnect with a low sugar diet, we start to enjoy the natural sweetness of what's in it.

'However, there is good news for chocolate fans. The old wives tale about a bit of dark chocolate being good for us has some truth in it. It's to be applauded for its antioxidant content and has been proven to lower blood pressure. It's the food of the gods if it is eighty-five per cent cocoa.'

***

THESE RECIPES CONTAIN SMALL AMOUNTS OF NATURAL SUGAR

Apple Trifle

Take a small glass and add layers of stewed apples with no added sugar.
Natural Greek yogurt
No added sugar granola
Top with a drizzle of maple syrup

Black Forest Trifle

Take a glass and add layers of...
Pitted black cherries
Greek yogurt
Grated 70% cocoa dark chocolate
Top with grated dark chocolate.

Figgy Pudding

Slice two figs in half.
Top each half with a teaspoon of Greek yogurt or mascarpone cheese. Top with chopped toasted almonds and a drizzle of maple syrup.

***

Salt

It's on every restaurant and cafe table, so we are conditioned to add salt to our food from a young age. However, the more we get used to doing it routinely, the more it masks the flavour of the foods we are eating and removes the pleasure of tasting them. Use a little seasoning in cooking, but never add it to a plate of food until you have tried the food first. Furthermore, high levels of salt in our diet increase the risk of high blood pressure, which can lead to heart disease.

Fred explains, 'DASH (Dietary Approaches to Stop Hypertension) has proved that salt is connected to our blood pressure. If our blood pressure isn't good, it can lead to strokes and heart attacks and osteoporosis.

'It's associated with improving the flavour of food but it's a bit like having a sweet tooth – the more salt we have, the less we taste it. So you can get into a spiral of more consumption. That's why we like our salted peanuts more than we like our peanuts. We hit that pleasure button far beyond our need for salt. The least we can get away with is the right amount.'

***

Caffeine

There is joy to be had from a freshly brewed pot of tea or coffee but we should regulate our caffeine intake to prevent dehydration and regulate our sleep pattern and therefore, our energy levels.

'Don't drink too much caffeine and I don't think it should be consumed after 2pm,' says Fred. 'The half life of caffeine in the body is three to four hours, depending on our genetics. So if we have a coffee at 7pm, we still have half the caffeine content in our body at 10pm, disturbing our sleep. A maximum of two or three caffeinated drinks a day is the right way to go.'

Sports Nutrition Supplements

Eager for progress, I have encountered many clients who arrive hoping to increase their training output and results, maybe a faster run, a new lifting PB, by adding a pre-workout to their diet just before hitting the gym floor. However, the more an amateur athlete relies on these for training, the less they have a true picture of what their body is capable of, so it's a good move to not fall into a pattern of taking a pre-workout routinely before training. They can also add to the risk of over training, masking muscle fatigue and causing injury. For these reasons, most amateurs don't need them at all.

'In general athletic development in amateurs,' says Fred, 'they need enough sleep, enough protein, enough of the right kind of calories and enough training. Nine times out of 10, the limiting factor in the amateur group is enough of the right kind of training. So many think if they take a pre-workout and some protein powder, they will grow muscle quicker and exercise 30 hours a week. I think protein powder is a poor supplement for most people. We should be able to get our protein from our normal whole food. It doesn't have to be expensive. It can come from eggs or pulses. Vegans find it harder but it's still perfectly attainable. Non vegans can also get it from lean white meat and fish.

'Professional athletes that I work with are likely to be training smart for 15 hours a week. I don't support clients with sports nutrition until they are up to eight to 10 hours a week of high output exercise. At that point, even a great diet won't support their recovery requirements. Most people can recover with a rest day in training. If a professional athlete is training twice a day, they can't do that and sports nutrition has a role to play here.'

'Creatine is only helpful for professional power based athletes. It works if it is taken properly,' says Fred. 'Strength related training, explosive movement and a need to improve a one rep max can be assisted by creatine. If this isn't your area, there isn't a huge amount of benefit. Nor is there a huge benefit to amateur athletes or endurance athletes.'

***

Diabetics

A well balanced nutritional diet can help diabetes type 1 patients control their insulin requirement and have a rigorous role to play in eliminating a diabetes type 2 diagnosis.

Fred explains the difference between the two and the valuable part sound nutrition plays here.

Type 1 diabetes
'This disease cannot be rescued nutritionally, though good nutrition certainly helps. With type 1, we need a low sugar, low alcohol, regular exercise, good for your gut microbiome diet. This means lots of wholegrain, no white processed food, lots of fruit and vegetables. We certainly don't want to be overweight. Be aggressive about activity to drive fat mass down and have a good exercise volume.'

Type 2 diabetes
'If we are a newly diagnosed type 2, we have an 80 per cent chance of no longer being diabetic if we lose 15 kilos. It is quite a lot to lose but it is a disease of obesity and a long-term health risk. If we are a type 2 diabetic, our chances of having a heart attack are the same as a non-diabetic who has already had a heart attack. If we get the excess weight off, it will help enormously. We can do blood tests which show how much work the pancreas is capable of and we occasionally find people have type 2 because their pancreas is poor functioning. That may be less recoverable. For most type 2 people, even though their pancreas is working very hard, it can't produce enough insulin to counter their poor diet. Improving nutrition here can make an immense difference to well-being.'

***

I Did It My Way
'It took seven rounds of IVF treatment, six years and all our life savings before I conceived our daughter, Betsey, who is now two years old. It was a tough journey. Every new round of treatment felt like an exam that I couldn't

revise for. I felt out of control of what was happening. In the run up to each attempt, there were blood tests and scans every day and it was physically and emotionally exhausting. IVF isn't a guaranteed science and you never know if it will work. Every time my partner and I tried, we did so without knowing whether there would be a happy ending. And we kept getting bad news. I felt like such a failure for so long.

'I didn't tell anyone about my first miscarriage. Afterwards, I went to work at the This Morning studios as usual and was asked to hold a baby, for a bonniest baby competition. It was unbearable. We don't talk about the loss of a baby enough. I confided in Amanda Holden and she suggested counselling, which I'd recommend. I had felt so isolated. When I spoke about my experiences on television, so many women came forward to say they had been through the same emotional pain.

'The cut off age for treatment was 47 and I finally conceived aged 46. My partner Paul and I made a decision to keep going until we were told to stop and worked all the hours to finance IVF. If you are considering fertility treatment, my advice is to find a doctor who is in your corner. Crucially, work out how much you and your partner can take emotionally, physically and financially. All the way through, I did my best to look after my body and also exercised through my pregnancy. I ran until I was no longer able to and did online ballet classes. I started to run again three months after the birth of our daughter and still run most days now. It's so good for my physical and mental health. I made sure I ate well and kept a careful eye on my nutrition, to maximise my chances of conception. And though it wasn't always at all easy, I tried to keep a positive mindset.' –
Sharon Marshall

YOUR NEXT STEP

HALF the problem with wanting to instigate change is deciding what you want to achieve and how you could feel more fulfilled. Think about what makes you happy, where your skill set is and if you need to add to it. The easy part of this is how. The action can be broken down into stages, research can be done and you can move towards your purpose gradually.

Size doesn't matter here. Don't be afraid to think big. Conversely, it may be one small change that you have been putting off, that will make a meaningful difference to your life. Ask these questions:

What do I want less of in my life?
What do I want more of?
Where in my week can I make time to get started?
Do I need help to find courage?

If you already have a specific goal, commit to it and take the first step towards it, today.

***

Strength and Power

In order to have the energy to achieve your goal, you will need physical functional fitness, to make sure all of the must do, often mundane, tasks in your life are taken care of efficiently, so that you have enough residual energy for what you want to achieve for yourself and not zone out on the sofa.

Look at your relationship with nutrition. Is there enough of the right fuel in your engine? Are you hydrated? Do you need to curb alcohol consumption? Do you need further help with any of these?

Are you getting enough exercise? Moving your body regularly is vital. By increasing your heart rate safely, you release endorphins, inducing a sense of calm and suppressing the stress hormone, cortisol.

Getting these vital elements, regular exercise and good nutrition, working together, creates physical endurance and mental strength. Combining these and being mindful of maintaining them will enable mental agility, so that you can manage any life hurdles that come your way, without losing sight of your personal objectives and passions.

Fitness is my job but it's also vital for my life and my health. I get to do the things I love because I maintain my energy. I very much practice what I preach. When I am invigorated and getting good sleep, it's much easier to think clearly and problem solve before a situation escalates.

Where Do You Go From Here?

When life is busy but there is something I want to achieve, I find a way, by carefully managing my time.

When I am embarking on a new project, I look at my diary, and fully commit to it on my quieter days, ring fencing this time and giving it my full attention.

However, I also commit to chipping away at it, every day. I make a call, do a little research and keep moving towards my end goal.

You may need to book a course to expand your knowledge. I've done so many over the years, from learning Spanish to flying trapeze and flamenco. By doing so, immediately you surround yourself with others with the same common goal and varying degrees of proficiency, all from different backgrounds. Being around like minded people increases your inner strength and purpose.

Stop Procrastinating

Make a commitment and go for it. Stop delaying getting started and take the first step. It's easy to get diverted by other elements of our lives. If this happens, re-set your rudder and continue your journey.

Changing Direction

Don't be afraid to change direction. You may embark on your new found goal and discover that it moves or changes altogether, as your confidence and knowledge evolves. This is completely ok and just shows you are growing into your purpose and truly listening to what you really want for yourself. Change is something that some of us can handle better than others. Take your time. Do it your way.

Be Accountable

In order to stay on track, find an acceptable way to be accountable. Start with keeping a journal. Write a daily or weekly record of your achievements in a book or keep notes on your phone. As you move further along, every few weeks glance back to the beginning. It's a great motivator to see how far you have come. It's also a useful tool for measuring progress, identifying patterns of behaviour and recognising our strengths and weaknesses objectively.

If you are taking a course, it may be that there is homework you need to produce. Take constructive feedback for what it is and don't be damaged by it. Never take it personally.

Consider being accountable to a close friend. Check in with them regularly to discuss your journey and let them be your cheer leader as you progress. Accept the compliments when they come. You have earned them.

It's Never Too Late

Every day is a school day. We will never know everything and that is at the core of life's challenge. But the more we are willing to learn, the more we evolve as personalities and, in turn, the more interesting our lives become. I am inspired by anyone who is passionate about their job or interest, whether it's space travel or running a bakery, walking the Pennine Way or star gazing. We can always learn from others if we are prepared to make time to listen and are not afraid to ask questions. A genuine interest is rarely rebuked.

As well as passions, interests and careers, it's never too late to address wellness. Among my clients is an 82-year-old man with a heart condition. He joined one of my classes, always shows up, works consistently every week and does each new thing I ask of him. He made a commitment to his wellness and is reaping the rewards of his dedication, living a full, active life.

Impact Others

If you take a new step and feel willing and able, consider sharing it with others in your circle of friends. In doing so, you will inspire them. Like dropping a pebble into a pond, you will be amazed at how many positive ripples you will cause. When my clients share their fitness achievements on social media, it always prompts a positive response and each time, some of their friends join their fitness crusade, just because one person was brave enough to share their progress. Though this doesn't have to be about fitness. Just by making a commitment to your goal, others will perhaps consider their own personal ambitions. Never underestimate the impact you can have on others, just by following your own purpose.

Rewarding Resilient You

To keep motivated, reward yourself along the way. Make sure that you have regular treats. The choice of bonus is up to you but make sure it isn't detrimental to your end goal and doesn't compromise your resilience. Commitment isn't always easy. You may get side tracked or lose faith. If this happens, get back to your plan as soon as you can. If possible, take a day or even a few hours just for you, to re-establish your purpose and alter its direction if necessary. Keep working at it in whatever small way you can manage, so that your accomplishments continue to grow. The longer the pause, the harder it is to pick up the reins and carry on. Gift yourself small treats each week or month and maybe promise yourself a bigger reward when you have completed your task.

You've Got This

Believe in yourself. This is the big one and it's not always easy. Whatever it is you want to achieve, trust your gut instincts, remember why you are doing it, don't give up and get it done.

When I competed in adult ballroom and Latin medalist dance competitions, for a long time I was a bag of nerves as I stepped onto the dance floor. A coach once gave me a golden piece of advice. He told me to step onto the floor standing tall, believing I was going to win and had a right to be there. I stopped walking meekly, shyly taking up hold with my partner. Instead, I strode onto the floor with intent and a smile. I had done all the hard work in the practice room. This was just my chance to show it off. As my approach changed, so did my dancing, which didn't go unnoticed and I started to collect trophies.

When I wanted to cover the war in Bosnia as a young journalist, there were smirks from other news reporters. The duty deputy news editor Tony Bushby took me to one side, asked about my plan and discussed my commissions. Then he gave me a nod and said, 'Do it, you'll be fine, damn good war to cut your teeth on.' As I took on this dangerous trip, with no previous war reporting experience, I needed to hear those kind words.

Don't be surprised if some doubt your abilities or question your motives. Pay them no heed. Do not indulge their negative attention. If you want something badly enough, you can absolutely have it. Do your research. Prepare. Commit. And don't ever let anyone tell you otherwise.

***

I Did It My Way

'There are moments when it can be very stressful in a restaurant kitchen, when up to 20 chefs are working together to bring a plate to the pass at the same time. I think those in my industry enjoy the tension of service. Like an actor going out before an audience, it's a good rush of adrenaline. But balance is important. I feel very strongly that sport is a vital part of everyday life. Even half an hour of getting your heartbeat up and getting a sweat on is beneficial physically. For me, it's also important mentally. I call it the hygiene of life. It should be part of everybody's routine to find time to exercise. I have a very busy diary. If I can find half an hour, anybody should be able to. I like to exercise alone, probably because I am rarely on my own. Particularly at work, I am surrounded by people. I have no music and just get lost in my own breath, my heartbeat and can be at peace for 30 minutes. I feel invigorated afterwards.*
I have always enjoyed sport. At school, I was one of the few that liked to do cross country running. As a young man, like my colleagues in the

hospitality industry, I was working very long hours and partying hard, as well. I was drinking too much coffee, having too much alcohol, smoking and not leading a particularly healthy life. I was a grumpy chef and not sleeping well. Though even then I would occasionally run or play squash. I took up running more seriously when my daughter was born, 30 years ago. I gave up smoking and my running became more important. I used to suffer from terrible migraines. When I started to run regularly, my migraines disappeared completely. It cured all of that. My diet improved to support my running and I generally felt so much better. Mentally I had more clarity. There were no more sleepless nights and it was easier to make good decisions quickly. Everything changed for me.

I went through a phase where I ran marathons for fun, which I absolutely adored. My marathon days are most probably behind me now. I still run but not as much as I did. I usually run or go to the gym in the morning. I cannot imagine my life without exercise. I certainly never want to go back to being the unhealthy man I once was.' —
Michel Roux Jr

'I have always been very driven in my career. I'm also a wife and a mum to our son. When I became ill, I had to step back. My best advice is to be kind to yourself and take time to recover. During this time, do anything that makes you smile. You will get through it.'—
Desrin Wickington

'The most difficult part of my life was my divorce from my first wife. I sank into self pity and wasn't much use to anyone around me. I still had access to our son weekly but it wasn't the same as living with him. I was in my mid-40s. The people who invited my wife and I out as a couple stopped calling and my circle of friends shrunk. Eventually, I realised that the only person that could do anything about my life was me. No one was going

to do it for me. I didn't want a new partner, I just wanted to create a new life for myself. After two years of misery, I gradually started to live my life again. I went to the theatre and cinema on my own and started socialising. After four years, I met my second wife. I'm now in my ninth decade. I truly feel that it's never too late to do something with your life.' –
Ray Woodbury

LIFE LESSONS

WE all have our view on how we should be living our lives. With the availability of 24-hour news channels and social media, we can choose to be bombarded with the opinions of others, to be selective or to opt out. Over time, I've learned to smile politely when I hear a stance that is directly opposed to mine. On occasion, when that view strongly offends my moral compass, I've taken that person on and challenged them and I always will, because it feels like the right thing to do.

I've also been lucky enough to have people arrive in my life who have had my back, were encouraging and offered great guidance, both personally and professionally, for which I will always be extremely grateful. So I pass on my advice here with the caveat that it is entirely optional. Take the bits that you might find useful and act on them.

***

When Life Throws You a Grenade, You Can Let It Blow Up Your World, or Catch It and Run With It

When our world is tipped upside down, ripped apart and our heart aches, we have two choices. Fight or flight. We can run from that grenade, move to another city, change jobs, travel but it's only our physical geography that will change. The problem will continue to haunt you and create problems with future relationships until you confront it, pin it down, work through it, accept it and then you can move forwards. There is no weakness in these actions. It hasn't beaten you. Quite the opposite. Running away is the easy option. I did plenty of it when I was younger. Standing and fighting, working to a conclusion and all the heightened emotion this brings, is far harder but so much more rewarding. It doesn't change or lessen the impact of the grenade but in coming to terms with it, you will find peace.

Some Days You Just Can't and That's Ok. Try Again Tomorrow

During the Covid-19 pandemic, three of my closest friends died in quick succession. Between them, we shared over 50 years of friendship and adventure. When I lost the first friend, it hurt deeply. The second death compounded that pain. When the third followed a week later, the pain of loss became unbearable. I found myself bursting into tears at a moment's notice. All three had been ill for some years. I had tried my best to support these friends and their families for a long time and now felt empty and hollow. So I took some time off work. I grew vegetables, hugged my husband, baked bread, ate tasty food even when I had no appetite, stayed away from news reports, watched gentle comedies on television and listened to kind hearted podcasts. I took one day at a time. And though I will miss those three friends forever, gradually I healed.

I had an early miscarriage before the birth of my daughter. I ached for the loss of that baby and thought I would never get over it. I buried myself in work to disguise the pain, though medical professional friends told me to rest. Eventually, I sought bereavement counselling, with the gentle encouragement of my husband, mourned our lost baby and started to move forwards.

The more pressure we put on ourselves to perform for others when we are feeling compromised, the further we fall. It's not a helpful strategy. Some days, it's absolutely ok not to be ok.

My plan for difficult, painful times remains the same as it did on my darkest of days. I don't look back and don't look too far ahead. I concentrate on putting one foot in front of the other. Do this. Try again tomorrow and keep trying. Gradually, it will get easier.

Ask for Help

There are far more people in this world who want to help us than want to fight us. If you need practical help or advice, the internet will only take you so far. You can't fix everything on your own. Don't be afraid to ask. Reach out. Take that first step to healing your life.

I think this is probably the most important lesson I've learned. It may be that you need a sofa to sleep on or some help sorting out bills or someone who will listen without judgement and give you time and space to think. Asking for help forces us to consider a new pathway that may be challenging but might just lead to a whole new beginning, some serenity, maybe an adventure. Better the devil you know? If you're even asking that question, it's unlikely, isn't it?

Keep Throwing the Rope

If we see that someone is drowning in misery, our instinct is to throw them a rope, to help pull them out of despondency and towards us. It is their choice whether they choose to catch it. They may not straight away. But keep throwing the rope. One day, they just might. However, whether they do or they don't, is not your privilege. Nor is it your failure if they choose not to catch it. You have done your best. Let that be enough. A dear vicar friend gave me this advice some years ago and I think it brilliantly clarifies that we must accept our limitations.

One Change at a Time

If you want to change an aspect of your life, make a plan. Then break that plan into smaller, manageable, achievable steps. Chunk it down. Make lists. Get organised. Then make one change each week that is sustainable. Only add another when you feel ready and comfortable. If you try and make too many changes at once, they become overwhelming and are unlikely to be long lasting. Get advice and support if you need it. Build your well-being gradually, one block at a time.

Don't Repeat the Same Mistakes

I really like the saying, 'If you always do what you've always done, you'll always get what you've always got.' I made a decision during my recovery from cancer that if someone or something keeps me awake at night, using up my precious energy, I no longer want them or it in my life. The old me, would have carried on, trying to please others, worrying about the outcome of a situation that didn't sit right. I would have accepted invitations to places I really didn't want to be, for fear of offending. Well, that old me has gone. There is a good chance that those energy sapping people and situations would have slid out of my life on their own terms over time. Now, I choose to speed up the process by refusing them access to my life in the first place. Don't be afraid to say no, politely but firmly. It's empowering and the more you say it, the easier it gets. You don't need to lie or make excuses for your decision.

I've learned that by filtering out what I want less of in my life, I make space to be creative about what I want more of. Whether this means spending more time with people who think like I do, those I care about, a bit more time on my own, altering my work space or using my free hours to do something more fulfilling, I go right ahead and manage my time and energy to suit me. You can, of course, choose to not do this but must also accept that the outcome will always be uncomfortably familiar.

Me Time Is Important

We are often time starved, living busy lives. I've learned that it's ok to take time for me. It's not selfish. It makes me happy, calm and, in turn, a better person for those around me. By creating space to think and process, I release stress. I can then focus on the tasks ahead with renewed vigour, place them in order of priority and become more productive. I recognise when my energy is low and pull back. There was a time when I would push through this feeling until I was exhausted, in order to meet a deadline set by someone else. As a young new journalist, I would work all day on one newspaper, then work a nightshift on another. I kept that going most of the week, keeping Sundays for me and working again on Sunday night. I had bylines on every news stand and was delighted, though by Saturday night I could barely write my own name, never mind headline grabbing copy. In my 20s, I could bounce back after one good night's sleep. That certainly isn't the case now. Nor would I recommend that work ethic to anyone of any age. While my professional life was busy, my relationship choices were poor, and I was missing from most family and friends' gatherings. There was no balance in my life. When I was working on a story elsewhere in the country or overseas, I'd return to a cold flat with nothing in the fridge except sour milk and just the television to keep me company. Professionally I was kicking ass. Privately, I was lonely and unfulfilled. As I got older, I became choosy about the amount of work I took on and this changed completely when I met my husband. I had a light bulb moment and started to turn down work above what I needed to pay my bills, preferring a warm heart to a much fatter bank balance. I earned enough to get by and had a nice life. I didn't need more money or bylines. What I needed was time to laugh, dance and be held by a lovely human. When I started work as a fitness professional, it was tempting to work all the hours to please new clients. Instead, I allocated time for work and time for me. I'm happy and so are my clients.

Work to Live. Don't Live to Work

My professional achievements matter to me a great deal but I work to live. I don't live to work. I'm very proud of what I have achieved professionally, both as a journalist and with my Fitter Stronger business. But I'm far more proud of being a fairly decent mum and raising two content teenagers, a hopefully supportive wife and an available friend. There is no question that these things matter the most to me and I guard the time to make them happen. When my children were younger, I heard myself say, 'In a minute' far too often and took a conscious decision to make that stop. Of course, I'll ask them to wait a moment if I'm in the middle of something else. But I then come straight back to them and give them my full attention. It feels right to ring fence time for those close to me, time for me and the rest fits in. By prioritising, my to do list always gets done. The urgent stuff is taken care of first. The rest of it gets done the next day or next week.

Take a Chance

If I'm presented with an opportunity that sounds interesting, I ask myself 'What's the worst that could happen?' Then I think about how I'll feel once I've completed it. Next, I do my research and go for it. I have always learned something from a challenge. The most important lesson is usually that I'm capable of a little more than I thought, which gives me the confidence to push on and accept other new opportunities. I don't ever want to look back and ask myself, 'What if?' Nor do I want to wonder what something might have felt like, who I might have met or where it may have lead next. I'd much rather know that succeed or fail, I tried. I remind my children and those I coach of this, too.

Also, I've realised that I don't want to look back and see gaps in my knowledge that could have been filled. So I actively fill those gaps. During the Covid-19 pandemic, I missed flying on an aeroplane to visit new places. One of the things that was allowed to happen for a period was wing walking, so I signed-up at an Essex aerodrome. For many years, it had been an ambition of mine. I had flown long zip wires with friends who felt adrenaline when I didn't. When I mentioned this to a friend, she suggested that when I had cancer, I was the most frightened I had ever been, so maybe I wouldn't feel adrenaline again. But the rush came back to me as the engine turned over on the biplane in preparation for my flight, adding to the excitement. The flight was everything I hoped it would be and lead to another adventure, taking a flying lesson in a Tiger Moth.

Also, during the pandemic, when educational pursuits were allowed, I took a pottery course. I had wanted to activate the creative part of my brain, which had lain dormant since my school days. The first pot I threw resulted in me and the floor being covered in clay but I persevered and am now a keen ceramics convert. Before the Covid-19 lockdown, I joined an aerial fitness studio and took a course in aerial silks. Everyone else in the class was half my age or less. It would have been so easy to be intimidated but I wanted to learn and had developed enough strength and agility to give it a try. It was incredibly difficult but I loved the challenge and small improvements each week encouraged me to continue to learn.

The previous year, I booked a flying trapeze lesson, which was so exhilarating that I booked places for my two teenage children and we returned together. They loved performing a swing and catch and this lead to an animated conversation on the train home about all of the other things they want to try.

Fear Ruins Opportunity

We were discussing fear over dinner a couple of nights ago. My daughter asked me what I feared and I answered her honestly, nothing. She persisted, 'What about fire? No? Ok, rats? No?' and so it continued. I have reached a point in my life where nothing scares me.

This may have some link to my friend's theory that I have been scared for my life and maybe nothing can touch that fear, except the fear of losing those close to me. It may also have something to do with my learned fight or flight reactions, based on previous life experiences.

As a young woman, I was given an opportunity to work on a newspaper. I had a steady job in a record company, a reliable income and good life. It would have been so easy to say no, as I had no proven journalistic skill or experience at this point. If I had turned down that opportunity, I would have missed out on an incredibly exciting career that lasted the best part of three decades, fulfilling a childhood ambition and learning transferrable skills that I still use today.

The decision to take that risk was invaluable, led to priceless opportunities and changed the whole direction of my life. Don't ever let fear ruin opportunity.

Keep Lines of Communication Open

Communication is one of our most valuable tools as humans. As a journalist, I learned far more from listening than I did from speaking. So many times, I was told by another reporter or publicist to watch out for a particular interviewee because they were difficult to talk to. I rarely found that was the case and tried to always enter the room without any preconceived expectation about the person sat in front of me, either for better or worse. Keeping an open mind and listening was always the best way to learn something new. Usually, I was pleasantly surprised.

By applying the same approach in daily life, we can find common ground with the people we think we have least common currency with. There will doubtless be occasions where we find ourselves needing to work alongside people we don't know, maybe don't like or don't trust. It's at these times that good communication, vitally listening as well as talking, is at its most useful.

In my friendships, I often send messages, notes in the post or make telephone or video calls. My friends do the same for me. We check in on each other. We may not see each other for months or even years, especially if we live some distance apart, but the familiarity we have worked at means that when we do meet, we can sit and drink coffee together as comfortably as if we'd seen each other the day before.

Conversely, there are people who come into our lives to take our energy and time but are unavailable when we need them. Whether you continue putting effort into these friendships is up to you.

Live In the Moment

When I was ill, I trained myself to not look back, as I wasn't going there and to not anticipate too far ahead. Looking too far into the future was pointless as I had no idea what the future held and the options were peppered with what ifs. This approach can quickly escalate into catastrophising, causing anxiety. Instead, I'd try to concentrate on the events of the day ahead and managing those as best I could. This meant I gave myself space to notice when the sunny yellow daffodils poked their stems and through the ground and their flowers opened, heralding a change of the seasons from dark winter to brighter spring. It may not seem a lot to get excited about but those small happy things could change my mood entirely.

If we constantly hark back to where we came from or plan too far ahead, we miss out on the joy and opportunity right in front of us. If we are distracted and trying to do two things at once, we miss out on doing either properly. At my first Fitter Stronger Goes Wild retreat, I noticed how many times guests were looking at the wildlife in front of them through a tiny phone camera. I encouraged them to regularly put their phones in their pockets. They were never going to forget the crash of rhino or herd of elephants in front of them, so take a good, long look at their behaviour, put them in context, notice their environment, the fragrance of the bushveld, the warmth of the sun and be enveloped by that moment. This one move changed their outlook completely.

I try to consider each new day as a fresh opportunity to do something that will maybe be useful or pleasurable and make me smile. I have learned to truly value every sunrise and sunset and appreciate today. Crucially, I also commit to never wasting a day.

Exercise for Good Mental and Physical Health

For as long as I can remember, I have always loved to exercise, whether that means running races or competing at ballroom and Latin competitions or taking on the CrossFit Open, swimming, practising yoga, walking my dog, playing netball or hitting the gym. I like how it releases endorphins without fail, clears my head and helps me think clearly. I can't imagine life without it. If you are new to exercise, remember that there are lots of options. There is no such thing as not liking exercise, just finding the right exercise for you. You may find that you need to adjust your workouts as you get older. I used to find this frustrating. Now, I realise it has opened up a whole new world of exercise opportunity I hadn't tapped into previously.

The benefits of exercise are immense. As well as creating good mental and physical health, exercise helps us set goals and build confidence in ourselves, which are skills that we can transfer into other areas of our lives.

Nourish For Performance

As a young woman, my nutrition was fairly poor. There were too many takeaways and not enough vegetables. I frequently missed breakfast and ate late at night. I was eating at my desk, in the car, on the train and in front of the television. None of it was mindful or considered. As a result, I lacked energy, my skin and hair suffered and I craved weekend lie-ins. I have far more energy and better skin and hair, many years later, because I now feed my body the fuel is needs for functional fitness. I sleep well and wake alert, at the same time each day. If your job involves shift work, adjust your nutrition so that you are still having breakfast, lunch and dinner, with snacks, at regular times, to suit your working life. I've learned that no amount of exercise will help if our nutrition is consistently poor. But balanced nutrition and good exercise create the perfect storm, supporting each other and creating a happier, healthier body and mind.

Find People Who Motivate You

Stay away from negative people. As a young woman, I used to smile and keep quiet around people who were inconsiderate of others or - my least favourite - people who are polite to the face of others but damning of them to others in their circle. However, I always felt sullied by their behaviour and somehow complicit. It never sat comfortably with me. Now, I either call them out or side step them out of my life. I sleep better and don't feel compromised.

Nor will I be drawn into a fight. If two friends are having a disagreement, I'll talk to both but never about each other. It's their fight, not mine and I have no interest in taking sides.

I have learned that when I am true to myself, I find I am drawn to souls who have the same outlook, honesty, integrity and share my passions and that makes me very happy.

My Best Is Good Enough

I've accepted that there is only one of me and only 24 hours in a day. Sure, I can multi task but I much prefer giving one job my full attention. I do all I can each day, the very best way I know how and then I stop and get good rest to enable me to be alert for my tasks tomorrow.

I have learned that my best is good enough and I make sure my clients and children know this for themselves, too. I have yet to see a grave stone that reads 'She wished she could have worked harder.'

I own my decisions and don't torture myself about whether I could have done something better than I did. And I accept that I will be better at some things than others, as we all are, which makes the world the interesting place we live in.

Never, Ever, Give Up

Lastly, never, ever give up. Sometimes, we have a mountain to climb and it seems insurmountable. How we choose to climb it can make the difference between a calm mind and sleepless nights.

If you want something in your life but it just isn't happening for you, re-evaluate your approach. Do you need advice? Who could you discuss it with? Reposition your map, push forwards and own your decisions.

If you are in the eye of a physical or mental storm, go back to basics. Get through today the best way you can and then try again tomorrow. Trust your inner strength.

Life is precious and brief. How much you choose to live it is up to you.